S250 Science in Context
Science: Level 2

The Open University

TOPIC 3
Water and well-being: arsenic in Bangladesh

Prepared for the Course Team by Steve Drury

This publication forms part of the Open University course S250 *Science in Context*. Details of this and other Open University courses can be obtained from the Student Registration and Enquiry Service, The Open University, PO Box 197, Milton Keynes, MK7 6BJ, United Kingdom: tel. +44 (0)845 300 6090, email general-enquiries@open.ac.uk

Alternatively, you may visit the Open University website at http://www.open.ac.uk where you can learn more about the wide range of courses and packs offered at all levels by The Open University.

To purchase a selection of Open University course materials visit http://www.ouw.co.uk, or contact Open University Worldwide, Walton Hall, Milton Keynes MK7 6AA, United Kingdom for a brochure. tel. +44 (0)1908 858793; fax +44 (0)1908 858787; email ouw-customer-services@open.ac.uk

The Open University
Walton Hall, Milton Keynes
MK7 6AA

First published 2006. Second edition 2007. Third edition 2008

Edited and designed by The Open University.

Typeset by The Open University.

Printed and bound in the United Kingdom by Halstan Printing Group, Amersham.

ISBN 978 0 7492 2680 0

3.1

The S250 Course Team

Andrew J. Ball (*Author, Topic 2*)

John Baxter (*Author, Topic 6*)

Steve Best (*Media Developer*)

Kate Bradshaw (*Multimedia Producer*)

Audrey Brown (*Associate Lecturer and Critical Reader*)

Mike Bullivant (*Course Manager*)

James Davies (*Media Project Manager*)

Steve Drury (*Author, Topic 3*)

Lydia Eaton (*Media Assistant*)

Chris Edwards (*Course Manager*)

Mike Gillman (*Author, Topic 4*)

Debbie Gingell (*Course Assistant*)

Sara Hack (*Media Developer*)

Sarah Hofton (*Media Developer*)

Martin Keeling (*Media Assistant*)

Richard Holliman (*Course Themes and Author, Topic 1*)

Jason Jarratt (*Media Developer*)

Simon P. Kelley (*Author, Topic 2*)

Nigel Mason (*Topic 7*)

Margaret McManus (*Media Assistant*)

Elaine McPherson (*Course Manager*)

Pat Murphy (*Course Team Chair and Author, Topic 1*)

Judith Pickering (*Media Project Manager*)

William Rawes (*Media Developer*)

Shelagh Ross (*Author, Topic 7*)

Sam Smidt (*Author, Topic 7*)

Valda Stevens (*Learning Outcomes and Assessment*)

Margaret Swithenby (*Media Developer*)

Jeff Thomas (*Author, Topics 6 and 7*)

Pamela Wardell (*Media Developer*)

Kiki Warr (*Author, Topic 5*)

The Course Team would like to thank the following for their particular contributions:
Benny Peiser (*Liverpool John Moores University; Author, Topic 2*), David Bard
(*Associate Lecturer; Author, Topic 6*) and Barbara Brockbank (*Associate Lecturer;
Author, Topic 6 and Critical Reader*).

Dr Jon Turney (*University College London and Imperial College London*) was
External Assessor for the course. The External Assessors for individual topics were:
Professor John Mann (*Queen's University, Belfast*); Professor John McArthur
(*University College London*); Dr Richard Reece (*University of Manchester*); Dr Rosalind
M. Ridley (*University of Cambridge*); Dr Duncan Steel (*Macquarie University, Australia*);
Dr David Viner (*University of East Anglia*) and Professor Mark Welland FRS
(*University of Cambridge*).

Contents

In any civilised society, the first provision after a system
of laws is a safe and reliable water supply.

(Anon; believed to be from a Latin source)

Chapter I

Introduction: two tragedies

The *Yorkshire Gazette* of Saturday, 15 October 1825 (page 2), carried this harrowing story:

Most afflicting Calamity

On Friday, the 7th instant, a most melancholy accident occurred at Cloughton, near Scarbro', of which the following is a brief outline. Martha Outhwaite (Outhet), a married woman, and the mother of four children, on Thursday the 6th inst., (being market day at Scarbro') called upon a druggist of that place to purchase (as she expected) a packet of medicine [flour of sulphur] for herself and three children, as a preparative for the small pox, which at that time prevailed in the village of Cloughton.

It so happened, that before the packet was put up, a small parcel of arsenic, wrapped up for an individual of Wykeham, and placed on the counter, was by mistake carried off, notwithstanding the foreman of the shop had the precaution to mark in large characters the word 'poison' on the packet. On Friday night, about eight o' clock, this unfortunate mother mixed up the arsenic with a little treacle, in a small tin, and gave a tea-spoon-full to each child, viz. Jane, aged 5; Elizabeth aged 3½; and Martha, aged 2 years; and at the same time, took a somewhat larger quantity herself with a view to protect her infant son, 6 months old, at that time supported by the breast.

Shocking to relate, Jane died at eleven; Elizabeth at twelve; Martha at four and the mother at five, the same night and morning, after experiencing those agonies that are usually concomitant on mineral poisons. It is painful to add, that although the packet missing was supplied by a second, and immediate enquiry made from a crowded shop as to the packet lost, no intelligence could be obtained, until the fatal discovery as above. As the packet was boldly indorsed 'poison', it was presumed it would carry its own protection, whenever or wherever found; but alas! this unfortunate mother could not read.

A coroner's inquest was held at Cloughton on the above melancholy occasion, and a verdict of 'Accidental Death, occasioned by poison unconsciously and innocently administered and taken' was accordingly recorded. We cannot avoid remarking that a parcel containing arsenic, instead of being laid on the counter of a crowded shop, should have been carefully delivered to the person who ordered it; and that on its being missing, hand bills should have been immediately distributed through the market, and all the inns to make the circumstances as public as possible.

(*Yorkshire Gazette*, 1825)

In the early 19th century, arsenic was well known as a deadly poison; indeed, the precise fatal dose had been known since the time of the Roman Empire and possibly earlier. Its sulfides often occur in copper ores. When these ores were smelted at the dawn of the Bronze Age to make the alloy bronze, fatalities among metal workers would easily have been linked with the garlic smell of arsine gas (AsH_3) given off from the kiln. Arsenic sulfides are dull red and yellow in colour, unlike the metallic-looking sulfides of metals, so the source of the poisoning would be easy to track down. Curiously, the element had also been used medicinally from the 5th century BCE (before the Christian era): Hippocrates himself prescribed its sulfide in the treatment of boils and ulcers. A medicinal role remains to this day (Section 2.1). As a poison, arsenic is perfect: it is tasteless, and early symptoms include acute diarrhoea. Murder by arsenic poisoning could masquerade as natural death from cholera.

The use intended by the Scarborough druggist's customer from Wykeham is not recorded, but the arsenic was probably for killing rats. Some precaution was taken by labelling the package, but illiteracy was widespread in Britain at that time.

C R

■ What precautions against accidental poisoning would you expect in a chemist's or other shop today?

▨ It is highly unlikely that arsenic would even be stocked, let alone left on a counter. Any potentially poisonous drugs would need a doctor's prescription before being sold, against which the patient's name would be checked. Through the late 19th century until the 1970s, potential poisons were dispensed in bottles that were ribbed and brightly coloured, so even a person who could not read would know that the contents were unsafe. Today, even food and drink items on a supermarket shelf are exhaustively labelled with their contents. Potentially hazardous household items are also marked by distinctive icons.

C R E D

Today, such basic precautions are bound up with industrial and commercial ethics. Ultimate responsibility for pharmaceuticals lies with manufacturers, who must package them with clear statements of potentially harmful effects that are based on considerable research. Physicians must know their pharmacopoeia before prescribing, and pharmacists must double-check before dispensing. You could add that a duty lies with individual laypeople to heed warnings and ensure their safe use. But what of the 'safe and reliable water supply' in the quotation with which this topic began? Who is responsible for ensuring that domestic water supplies are indeed safe to drink?

In the UK, many people think that drinking water obtained from the kitchen tap is less of a pleasure than it used to be because the water supplied is among the most chlorinated in the world in order to protect us from bacterial, viral and parasitic biohazards. We take water safety for granted. From source to tap, the water travels from deep wells and large reservoirs through a series of sophisticated water-treatment plants and 'state-of-the-art' water-chemistry laboratories. Occasionally, things go wrong, such as in 1988 when excessive aluminium sulfate was accidentally added directly to the mains water supply at Camelford in Cornwall. Aluminium sulfate is routinely used in water treatment plants. During prolonged droughts harmful organisms can escape chlorination. London water has been subject to several 'boil before you drink' warnings. However, the fact that London water has already passed through several other people is no cause for alarm.

Over two-thirds of the world's population does not have such a comfortable relationship with their domestic water supplies. During the last three decades, people in two far poorer countries than Britain – Bangladesh and the state of West Bengal in neighbouring India – managed to escape centuries of premature death, most often childhood death from waterborne diseases, only to face the ultimate public-health tragedy of an even worse inorganic threat – that of arsenic poisoning. The aesthetic beauty of the surroundings often masks the hidden dangers beneath (Figure 1.1).

(a)

(b)

(c)

Figure 1.1   Images of Bangladesh: (a) the countryside; (b) village life; (c) traditional method of well sinking, which can penetrate soft sediment to a depth of more than 100 m.

Activity 1.1

Allow 60 minutes

Load the S250 DVD-ROM, select Topic 3, and listen to the audio band of the BBC's Radio 4 programme *Perfectly Poisoned*, which was first broadcast on 14 December 2004. It describes the emergence since the 1980s of endemic arsenic poisoning from drinking water in one of the most populous areas on Earth: West Bengal in India, and its neighbour Bangladesh.

By any standards, the tragedy emerging on the low-lying plains of the Indian subcontinent is not only poisoning on an unprecedented scale, but also a terrible case of 'out of the frying pan into the fire'. Before water from wells became the main supply for drinking, using surface supplies had been a cause of waterborne diseases for centuries, affecting children under 5 years of age in particular. As soon as well water became widely used, there was a dramatic fall in child mortality, only to be replaced a decade later by something far more insidious. It is now certain that tens of millions of Bengalis and Bangladeshis are at risk from arsenic contamination. Unlike the tragic death of the Outhwaite family, the poisoning of Bengalis and Bangladeshis was unforeseeable. Figure 1.2 shows graphically the affected areas in Bangladesh. A growing understanding of the causes of arsenic contamination highlights the rationale for even greater alarm, as similar geological conditions occur elsewhere. Up to 1.5% of the world population may be dangerously exposed to arsenic.

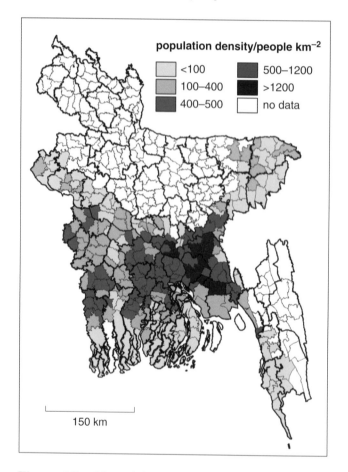

Figure 1.2   Map of the population densities in those districts of Bangladesh where well water is contaminated by arsenic (>50 μg l^{-1}). The key indicates each affected district's population density in number of people per square kilometre. Those areas shown in white are not affected by arsenic contamination. The thick black lines show the major administrative districts; thin black lines show the minor administrative districts.

Perfectly Poisoned sets the scene in general terms for this topic. *Water and well-being* will explore many factors involved in the tragedy through the scientific background and the course themes. In Chapter 2 you will learn about the basic chemical factors that underlie the hazard posed by arsenic, together with an investigation of the risk from drinking contaminated water. Chapter 3 covers the geoscientific aspects, such as an introduction to underground water (groundwater) in Bangladesh and the geochemical conditions that help dissolve arsenic. Chapter 3 also examines risk from other standpoints: the way in which arsenic concentration varies from place to place in Bangladesh, and how research there allows geoscientists to predict where similar problems may remain undiscovered. You already know from Activity 1.1 that there were problems with communication as the arsenic tragedy unfolded, and you should have inferred that there is an important ethical dimension, considering the consequences (Chapter 4). The practical issue, now that the tragedy has revealed itself, concerns deciding how to mitigate the effects of arsenic poisoning (Chapter 5).

Activity 1.2 (Part 1)

Ongoing

As discussed in the *Introduction to the course*, we have adopted margin icons in the early part of the course to draw your attention to material that is particularly relevant to one or more of the themes. Following from similar activities in Topics 1 and 2, on ethical issues and decision making respectively, in Chapters 2–5 your focus will be on *communication*. We will therefore use the margin icons for risk, decision making and ethical issues – but not that for communication. Instead, *you* should write the letter C in the margin adjacent to text that you consider to be particularly relevant to communication of matters relating to contamination of water by arsenic. You should also make notes to remind yourself of the way(s) you consider the material to be relevant. We will return to this activity at the end of Chapter 5 in order to review what you have achieved.

C R E D

Chapter 2

Chemical elements and health

R   In this chapter, you will review some basic chemistry that is directly relevant to the way in which arsenic has come to be a hazard to not only humans, but to all animals. It does not just 'happen to be' a poison; the reason arsenic is poisonous raises the fascinating topic of the way in which biological evolution has been interwoven with changes in the inorganic chemistry of the Earth's surface environment. First, you need to know something about the chemical 'knife-edge' on which well-being and illness maintain an uneasy balance, which lies at the heart of risk in this context.

2.1 Elements: how much we need and what levels pose health threats

Ultimately, all elements involved in living processes come from the Earth itself: rocks and soils, water, and the atmosphere are linked with the living world by the rock cycle. Animals and plants have optimum requirements for between 20 and 32 naturally occurring elements. If these needs are significantly over- or under-supplied, ill health may result. A good example is the element fluorine or, more precisely, the fluoride ion (F^-) in aqueous solution. Natural decomposition or weathering of fluorine-bearing minerals releases fluoride ions that end up in surface and subsurface water. Our bodies need fluoride within a range of low concentrations to maintain strong bones and teeth: tooth enamel and bone tissue include a compound of calcium, fluorine, phosphorus and oxygen (fluorapatite) that is very strong. At lower concentrations in our diet, tooth decay and osteoporosis (low bone density) become common problems. At concentrations above the essential range, excessive bone formation and calcification of ligaments (sclerosis) start to occur after prolonged exposure. The first sign of excess fluoride in human diets is a brownish discoloration of teeth, especially in children (Figure 2.1a). The clinical result of prolonged ingestion of too much fluoride is fluorosis. In adults, renewed bone growth as nodules, irregular masses (Figure 2.1b) and sometimes spiny outgrowths that puncture the skin results in extremely painful conditions that are sometimes fatal. Accelerated bone growth due to high fluoride ingestion by children results in joints becoming enlarged and fused, leading to gross deformities (Figure 2.1c).

R   This dependence of health on the concentration of a particular element can be represented schematically on a **dose–response curve** (Figure 2.2). The effects of the element on the organism are represented by the vertical axis and the concentration of the element is represented on the horizontal axis. Although the concentration of an element can be quantified, assigning 'numbers' to the response is difficult, as explained later in this chapter. So, Figure 2.2 is not a 'graph' in the conventional sense, but a graphic means of conveying the concentration ranges that pose risks and those that are 'safe' and often necessary for well-being.

Below concentration A in Figure 2.2, the organism presents symptoms of some form of deficiency disease. A well-known example of a deficiency disease is

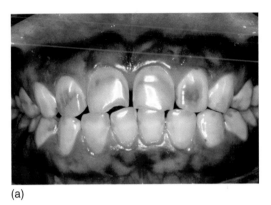

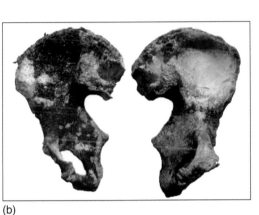

(a)

(b)

(c)

Figure 2.1   Symptoms of fluorosis: (a) discoloration of teeth; (b) abnormal bone outgrowths on the pelvis of an Icelander who died shortly after the Laki volcanic eruption in 1783; (c) girl with swollen knee joints due to fluorosis.

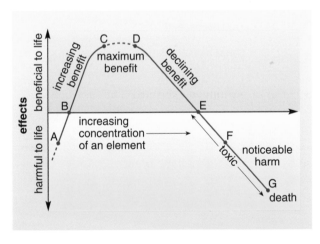

Figure 2.2   A generalised dose–response curve for an element according to its concentration in a regular diet. See text for explanation.

anaemia, which is caused by a deficiency in iron. Goitre results from insufficient iodine in the diet. In this disease, the thyroid gland swells in a vain attempt to produce sufficient thyroxine, which is the iodine-containing hormone that controls the rate of metabolism. The optimum concentrations of an element for health lie in the region between C and D on Figure 2.2. Concentrations higher than D cause declining benefit until, at concentration F, harmful effects are noticed; and at still higher concentrations, death may result (concentration G). Well-known examples of hazardous element excess, or **toxicity**, are lead, cadmium and mercury poisoning that result from industrial pollution or their former inclusion in much-used materials, such as lead in paints and petrol. Concentrations between

A and B and between E and F are of particular concern for many elements. They *may* be harmful to life, but no symptoms show themselves: the effects are said to be subclinical. Equally, the effects on well-being of concentrations between B and C (possibly increasing benefits) and between D and E (possibly decreasing benefits) are blurred: no harm is done, but the organism may not be functioning at the peak of efficiency.

The concept of a dose–response curve is useful, but is not easily quantified, partly because different individuals have slightly different responses. It is rarely possible to define precisely the points A to G for any element. The World Health Organisation (WHO) tries to establish recommended minimum and maximum concentrations (B and E respectively on Figure 2.2), but that is not an exact science, as you will see. Table 2.1 summarises the most common clinical effects of deficiencies and excesses of several elements.

Table 2.1 Some of the effects of element deficiencies and excesses in humans. Not all these elements pose toxic threats from their occurrence in water, as some are relatively insoluble. Those that may pose problems in drinking water are followed by (W). For the health effects of arsenic, see Section 2.2.1. Several medical terms are used for brevity, rather than describing how the condition presents; if you are interested in further study, use them as internet search terms.

Element	WHO maximum safe limits/mg l^{-1}	Effects of deficiency	Chronic effects of excess
aluminium, Al (W)			Alzheimer's syndrome?
antimony, Sb (W)		none	heart disease
arsenic, As (W)	0.01	possible link to retarded growth	see later text
barium, Ba (W)	0.07		high blood pressure (hypertension); muscular weakness
beryllium, Be (W)			lung cancer by inhalation*; bone damage
cadmium, Cd (W)	0.003	reduced growth?	hypertension; kidney damage (nephritis); severe joint pains; cancers
calcium, Ca		deformed bones; nerve and muscle spasms (tetany)	hardening of the arteries (atherosclerosis); cataract; gall stones
chromium, Cr (W)	0.05	corneal opacity; poor glucose metabolism	lung cancer by inhalation*
cobalt, Co		anaemia	heart failure; excess red blood cell production (polycythaemia)
copper, Cu (W)	2.0	anaemia; hair becomes kinky or depigmented	jaundice; damage to kidneys, brain, and eyes (Wilson's disease)*
fluorine, F (W)	1.5	poor bone and tooth development	mottled teeth; growth of excess bone (sclerosis)
iodine, I		under-active thyroid and depressed metabolism (hypothyroidism); goitre	overactive thyroid with many symptoms, such as muscle wasting, irregular heartbeat, anxiety (hyperthyroidism)

*Caused by industrial over-exposure.

Element	WHO maximum safe limits/mg l^{-1}	Effects of deficiency	Chronic effects of excess
iron, Fe		anaemia	iron build-up in the liver, heart and pancreas, to cause heart or liver failure (haemochromatosis); inflammation of the lung through iron build-up (siderosis)
lead, Pb (W)	0.01	none	anaemia; brain damage; nerve inflammation (neuritis); kidney cancer*
magnesium, Mg		convulsions	loss of consciousness; anaesthesia
manganese, Mn (W)	0.05	bones deformed; gonads affected; hair reddens	brain damage and lack of coordination (ataxia)*
mercury, Hg (W)	0.002	none	brain inflammation (encephalitis); neuritis*; memory loss; dementia
molybdenum, Mo (W)	0.07	reduced uric acid production and build up of toxins	growth depression
nickel, Ni (W)	0.02	dermatitis; liver changes	dermatitis; lung cancer by inhalation*
selenium, Se (W)	0.01	infertility; liver necrosis; muscular dystrophy	cancers; deformed nails and hair
silicon, Si		poor bone and cartilage growth	kidney stones; lung disease*
sodium, Na		weakness, confusion; collapse due to under-production of steroid hormones (Addison's disease); cramps	hypertension; heart failure
thallium, Tl (W)	0.002	none	hair loss; general numbness
tin, Sn		reduced growth	nerve damage
vanadium, V		serum cholesterol lowered	reduced growth
zinc, Zn (W)	3.0	dwarfism; immature gonads; dermatitis	anaemia

*Caused by industrial over-exposure.

Question 2.1

Sketch a schematic dose–response curve for fluoride similar to the one in Figure 2.2, given the following information. Concentration levels in drinking water of less than 0.05 mg l^{-1} have been shown to be associated with excessive dental decay. Those that range from 0.2 mg l^{-1} to 0.9 mg l^{-1} gives maximised benefit for healthy bone and tooth development. Concentrations above 1.5 mg l^{-1} are associated with stained teeth, then excessive bone formation and fluorosis.

RD

Setting maximum safe limits for a contaminant in drinking water (Table 2.1, Column 2) is a pragmatic and convoluted exercise. The approach used by the WHO is based on the lowest amount that is regularly ingested in milligrams relative to body mass in kilograms (giving units of $mg\ kg^{-1}$) that gives rise to adverse effects in animals dosed in laboratory tests (equivalent to concentration F on Figure 2.2). To account for the difference between the experimental animal and humans, and the adequacy of the experiments, this dosage is divided by an uncertainty factor (between 10 and 1000) to arrive at a *tolerable daily intake* (TDI) relative to body mass, in $mg\ kg^{-1}$. The concentration in drinking water that can be regarded as dangerous is then a product of the TDI, human body mass and the proportion (the decimal fraction, e.g. 10% = 0.1) of TDI that can be ascribed to drinking water, divided by the average daily intake of water in litres:

$$\text{maximum safe limit} = \frac{\text{TDI} \times \text{body mass} \times \text{proportion ascribed to drinking water}}{\text{daily water intake}}$$

The units are given by $\dfrac{mg\ kg^{-1} \times kg \times proportion}{l} = mg\ l^{-1}$

■ Apart from the obvious uncertainties in this empirical approach, is there any other cause for concern, with respect to Figure 2.2?

▢ It does not take into account the range of concentrations between E and F, which might present some unknown risk.

There is another pragmatic approach to estimating dangerous concentrations of elements in drinking water supplies. Unusually high incidences of specific ailments in some areas can stimulate research into their causes, as in the discovery that kuru in Papua New Guinea stemmed from a cannibalistic practice and a transmissible spongiform encephalopathy disease (Topic 1). The recognition of the association of fluorosis with high levels of fluoride in the diet of victims resulted from research into the chemistry of soils and drinking water in endemic fluorosis areas. Once a connection has been established between ill health and a particular element in drinking water, medical records of the ailment can then be compared with the concentrations in drinking water to which a victim has been exposed (Question 2.1). Natural concentrations vary, so it might seem possible to deduce concentrations E to G on the dose–response curve from the number and severity of clinical cases relative to concentration. In the case of fluoride, the effects are fairly simple and stem only from high fluoride ingestion, ranging through different degrees of tooth discoloration to the onset of excessive bone growth. However, establishing a safe upper limit of fluoride concentration in drinking water is complicated by the fact that fluorosis is a *progressive* condition: it worsens with time and the *rate* at which symptoms appear is connected with fluoride concentration. As you will see in Section 2.2.1, progressive arsenic ingestion induces a far larger range of ailments than fluoride, some specifically due to arsenic but others that also have other causes. Addressing the risks that people face from the chemical contamination of their environment is especially problematic. Generally, chemical risk is a combination of three factors:

- the **hazard** – what poses a threat, what it does, and why

- the **exposure** – the concentration of the hazard, how often it is encountered, and where that is likely to occur

- the **consequences** – dependent on the hazard and the exposure, but complicated by the fact that there is often a delay between a cause and its tangible symptoms while the offending element gradually affects healthy functioning of the body. The extreme consequence is death, which might arise soon after a single very high dose. In cases of cumulative doses that are less hazardous, death may be inevitable, but only after a long period of worsening chronic symptoms, victims of which become unable to live normally.

As you will discover in Section 2.3, the early stages of chronic arsenic poisoning appear several years after the start of exposure to concentrations far lower than a single fatal dose. The symptoms can be horribly disfiguring. Up to 20 years later, a range of physiologically more serious conditions may emerge, culminating in premature death. You might well ask which of the two, acute or chronic poisoning, is the worse consequence.

So far, you have looked at risk from human intervention in natural processes (for example prion diseases in Topic 1) over which we have considerable control once the hazard becomes apparent. In Topic 2, the hazard was from uncontrollable astronomical processes; but, given data on NEOs, risk can be assessed quite rigorously. Risks associated with contamination of water supplies that result from human activities, such as pollution due to metal mining and waste disposal, can be assessed and controlled easily once the problem is recognised. The sources and flow of pollution are predictable. As you saw in Chapter 1, the risk from arsenic contamination of water from wells in West Bengal and Bangladesh results from common natural processes that are less easily predicted, and came to light only in the last two decades of the 20th century. Uncovering the geographic extent of the problem requires a great deal of research. In Section 2.2 we look mainly at the chemical hazard posed by arsenic, including the crucial scientific question 'Why is arsenic poisonous?', touching on the issues of exposure and consequences in Section 2.3. But that by no means completes the assessment of risk from waterborne arsenic. It also requires some understanding of how elements move, accumulate and are released into the natural environment, and how geoscientists can begin to visualise the risk that stems from *where* people happen to live. These aspects are central to Chapter 3.

Often, the initial discovery of a waterborne hazard is made by individuals or small groups. They are powerless to make a full response themselves, but will inform those who can, namely governmental authorities. Response by responsible authorities would involve:

- assessing the occurrence of medical conditions due to the waterborne hazard

- discovering the extent of the problem, i.e. water with concentrations above WHO guidelines

- warning people likely to be at risk

- instituting remedial measures or evacuating people from hazardous areas.

Question 2.2

What problems might arise in using WHO guidelines for water quality (Table 2.1) in countries less well-developed than those in North America or Europe?

E

You should also begin to think about the ethical responsibilities of individual scientists or scientific institutions, whose training, experience and access to the best available analytical facilities make them authoritative on water quality. For instance, is there any reason why the same advanced techniques should not be applied in monitoring water quality anywhere? This is a question for you to ponder on, especially in Chapter 4.

2.2 Why are some elements poisonous?

The title of this section is one of the most difficult questions for a biochemist or a molecular biologist to answer. They would need to go into each element's fundamental properties, the entire scope of metabolism from cells up to whole organisms, and the chemistry of proteins (and other molecules) that are the essence of all living processes. Most proteins incorporate metals (such as iron and metals with similar chemical properties) and non-metals (such as sulfur and phosphorus), as well as linkages between carbon, hydrogen, oxygen and nitrogen, the principal elements for life. We look first at those elements that are essential to life, noting that excesses or deficiencies of each may cause health problems. You will see that the chemical environment in which life evolved has not always been the same as today. Elements that are poisons but which have little if any role in cell processes, such as arsenic, often became available in aqueous solution late in the history of life.

All organisms require about 20 of the 91 naturally occurring elements (Figure 2.3) to function, and the range increases to 32 with the inclusion of some odd kinds of metabolism. For instance, sea squirts use a vanadium-based protein as an oxygen carrier in their blood, akin to the iron-rich haemoglobin used in mammalian circulation. About 96.2% of our living body mass is made up of just four elements: oxygen (O, 65.0%); carbon (C, 18.5%); hydrogen (H, 9.5%) and nitrogen (N, 3.2%). Sodium (Na), potassium (K), calcium (Ca), magnesium (Mg), manganese (Mn), phosphorus (P), sulfur (S) and chlorine (Cl) make up 3.7%. Of the remaining 0.1% (trace elements), nine other elements are required by all organisms, and eleven more are essential to a few (Table 2.2).

Table 2.2   Trace elements (and their chemical symbols) involved in living organisms.

iron, Fe	zinc, Zn	fluorine, F	strontium, Sr
copper, Cu	selenium, Se	cadmium, Cd	nickel, Ni
silicon, Si	antimony, Sb	cobalt, Co	boron, B
bromine, Br	vanadium, V	tungsten, W	arsenic, As
chromium, Cr	molybdenum, Mo	iodine, I	barium, Ba

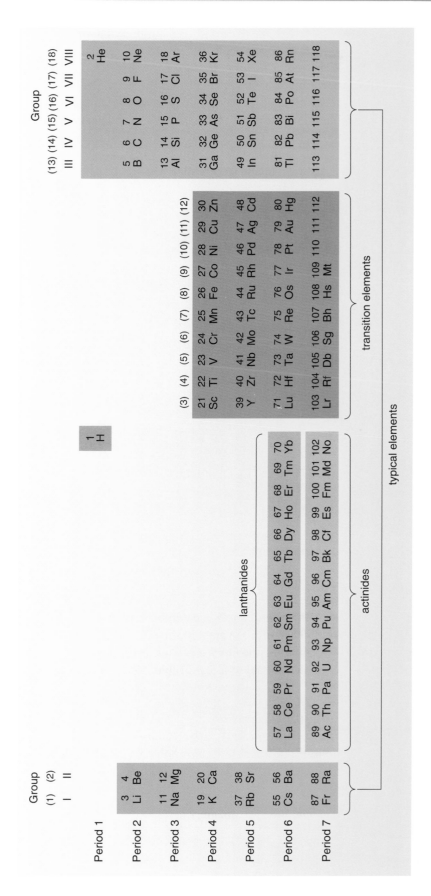

Figure 2.3   The Periodic Table of the elements. The groups (including the transition elements), lanthanides and actinides, collect together elements with similar atomic structures, and thus similar chemical properties. The numbers in brackets are the groups adopted by the IUPAC.

The presence of arsenic in Table 2.2 may surprise you, but brown marine algae and ferns accumulate it with no ill effects. It also seems to be essential for growth in some vertebrates, including mammals, albeit at minuscule concentrations. In fact, all 91 naturally occurring elements can be detected in healthy organic matter. However, the presence of about two-thirds of these elements is probably attributable to the cell's inability to completely exclude them rather than their playing any role in metabolism. Indeed, some biological systems concentrate elements even though they do not need them, an example being silver birch trees that concentrate zinc and lead in their leaves.

The group numbers 1–18 were adopted in 1984 by the International Union of Pure and Applied Chemistry (IUPAC).

A quick check against the Periodic Table (Figure 2.3) shows that, except for molybdenum (Mo), iodine (I) and tungsten (W), all the elements essential to life of one form or another have low atomic numbers (<36). They comprise members of Groups I to VII (sometimes called Groups 1, 2 and 13–18) and include the transition elements (sometimes called Groups 3–12). The noble gases (Group VIII, sometimes called Group 0 or Group 18), lanthanides and actinides have no known biological role.

The chemical properties of biologically useful elements are intimately bound up with the chemistry of living processes. A crucial point is that the biosphere has evolved within the wider scope of the Earth's other 'spheres'. As you will see shortly, the inorganic conditions of the lithosphere, hydrosphere and atmosphere evolved too. Organic evolution involved 'chemical opportunism' that was based primarily on the huge chemical diversity of polymers that mainly incorporated the elements C, H, O, N, P and S. Even more biochemical opportunities arose when other elements enter those molecules. The response of cells to changing environmental chemistry has been analogous to that of whole organisms to changing habitats.

To play a biological role, elements must be:

- chemically 'fit for purpose'
- sufficiently abundant to be in continual contact with cells
- available for cell processes. Since these are governed by the presence of water, elements must form or be included in soluble ions to play a role.

Most elements can enter aqueous solution to some extent, but whether or not they do so depends on some fundamental chemical properties. Dissolved ions can potentially pass through the membrane that surrounds the cell. Some of them can be co-opted to play a role in processes within cells, according to their properties. These become essential, within some biologically acceptable range of concentrations. Others that enter, which can play no role or are potentially toxic, need to be 'pumped' out as fast as they enter the cell, as do excesses of biologically essential elements. If that removal fails, then the cell dies or processes within it malfunction. The membrane surrounding a cell is associated with electrical gradients that serve as a means of pumping ions into and out of the cell. Central to this cellular 'pumping' is the back and forth movement of hydrogen in the form of H^+ ions (protons). Movement of electrons (e^-), and therefore negative charge, is also an essential part of cell processes. Electrons play a very important role in both organic and inorganic chemical processes, as you will learn from Box 2.1.

Box 2.1   Oxidation and reduction

You may have come across the terms oxidation and reduction in your earlier studies in relation to the relative proportions of oxygen and hydrogen in compounds:

- **oxidation** involves an increase in the proportion of oxygen or a decrease in the proportion of hydrogen in a compound
- **reduction** occurs when oxygen decreases or hydrogen increases.

Iron is *oxidised* to iron oxide by reaction with oxygen, for example iron railings may rust away.

$$4Fe(s) + 3O_2(g) = 2Fe_2O_3(s) \tag{2.1}$$

Ethanol (an alcohol) is *oxidised* to ethanoic (acetic) acid by reaction with oxygen, for example if a bottle of wine is left open to the air for too long.

$$CH_3CH_2OH(l) + O_2(g) = CH_3COOH(l) + H_2O(l) \tag{2.2}$$

Iron oxide is *reduced* to metallic iron by reaction with hydrogen. This is an expensive way of smelting iron.

$$Fe_2O_3(s) + 3H_2(g) = 2Fe(l) + 3H_2O(g) \tag{2.3}$$

Ethanoic acid is *reduced* to ethanol by reaction with hydrogen. This is an expensive way of making alcohol.

$$CH_3COOH(l) + 2H_2(g) = CH_3CH_2OH(l) + H_2O(l) \tag{2.4}$$

An alternative way of looking at each of the reactions in Equations 2.1 to 2.4 is by considering whether the *other* compound on the *left*-hand side of each equation has been oxidised or reduced.

■   What happens to the oxygen involved in Equations 2.1 and 2.2?

■   In the resulting compounds in both Equations 2.1 and 2.2, the proportion of oxygen is less than in the oxygen molecule itself, so the oxygen has been reduced.

■   What happens to the hydrogen in Equations 2.3 and 2.4?

■   In Equations 2.3 and 2.4, hydrogen has combined with oxygen to both reduce the proportion of hydrogen and increase that of oxygen in a compound, so hydrogen has been oxidised.

The simple definitions of oxidation and reduction work in these examples, and show that oxidation and reduction are inseparable. However, some other factor not shown in these equations drives these oxidising and reducing reactions. A closer look at Equation 2.1 reveals what that is.

■   In Equation 2.1, there is no charge associated with either iron or oxygen (the reactants) on the left-hand side. In iron oxide (the product, and an ionic compound), the charge on the oxygen is −2, in other words oxygen is O^{2-}. So what is the charge on the iron in iron oxide?

■ The iron oxide Fe_2O_3 must be neutral, so that the total charge carried by two Fe balances the total of -6 associated with three O. So the charge on each Fe must be $+3$, corresponding to the Fe^{3+} ion, for the charges in the formula to balance.

There is another, more fundamental definition of the difference between oxidation and reduction, illustrated by Equation 2.1. Metallic iron and oxygen gas are electrically neutral, i.e. they have zero charge. In the process of being oxidised, iron has *lost* electrons to acquire its $+3$ charge, whereas the oxygen has *gained* electrons in being reduced to O^{2-}. There is, therefore, a more general pair of definitions: *oxidation involves* the *loss of electrons*, whereas *reduction involves* the *gain of electrons* (Remember **OILRIG**: **O**xidation **I**s **L**oss; **R**eduction **I**s **G**ain).

- **Oxidising conditions** require the presence of an element or compound that tends to *accept* electrons: oxygen is a common **oxidising agent**.
- **Reducing conditions** require an electron *donor*: hydrogen is a common **reducing agent**.

But it is important to remember that there are other oxidising and reducing agents, such as the elements chlorine and carbon respectively and many compounds of several elements.

The reason that iron oxide in the form of Fe_2O_3 can exist is because iron and oxygen are bonded ionically. Iron carries positive charges and oxygen carries negative charges, and those charges must balance. But there is another iron oxide, FeO, which is also ionically bonded. You should be able to deduce that, in this case, iron has a charge of $+2$, so that Fe^{2+} ions bond with O^{2-} ions to form this oxide of iron. Because Fe^{3+} has lost one more electron than Fe^{2+}, it is the *more oxidised* of the two ions of iron. Iron has two **oxidation states**, formally known respectively as iron(III) and iron(II) when they are present in compounds. So, Fe_2O_3 is iron(III) oxide and FeO is iron(II) oxide. An important difference between the two oxidation states of iron is that ionic compounds of iron(III) are much less soluble than those of iron(II). Iron(II) oxides, and iron(II) hydroxides in particular, are unstable in the presence of water, whereas iron(III) oxides and hydroxides are extremely stable. As you will see in Chapter 3, that difference is crucial in the context of arsenic contamination of drinking water.

Iron is by no means the only element whose ions can be in more than one oxidation state. Hydrogen when in chemical combination always has a $+1$ state, and oxygen in combination always has a -2 state, but what about sulfur?

■ What oxidation state does sulfur have in (a) H_2S (hydrogen sulfide gas) and (b) SO_4^{2-} (sulfate ions)?

■ (a) In H_2S, sulfur is in a -2 state (reduced); (b) in sulfate ions sulfur has a $+6$ state (oxidised). (Two negative charges from the oxygen are unbonded, leaving -6 with which the sulfur is bonded.)

Other examples of non-metals with different oxidation states include:

Nitrogen N: in ammonia NH_3, the N is in a −3 state (reduced); in the nitrate ion NO_3^-, the N is in the +5 state (oxidised). (One negative charge from the oxygen is unbonded, leaving −5 with which the nitrogen is bonded.)

Carbon C: in methane CH_4, the C is in a −4 state (reduced); in carbon dioxide CO_2, the C is in the +4 state (oxidised).

Metals grouped as transition elements, of which iron is one (Figure 2.3), tend to have several possible oxidation states. Like iron, they form different kinds of compounds under oxidising and reducing conditions. In the case of some transition metals, e.g. iron, nickel and cobalt, their most oxidised states form insoluble compounds, whereas under reducing conditions their ions are more soluble. Other transition metals, such as copper and zinc, behave in the opposite way. Some semi-metals, of which arsenic is one, can also be in more than one oxidation state.

Question 2.3

What oxidation state does arsenic have in: (a) arsine gas AsH_3; (b) arsenite ions AsO_3^{3-}; (c) arsenate ions AsO_4^{3-}?

(a) AsH_3 $As: -3$

(b) AsO_3^{3-}

O_3^{3-} $-2 \times 3 = -6 - -3$
                $= -3$

$As = +3$

(c) AsO_4^{3-}

$O_4^{3-} = -2 \times 4 = -8 - -3$
              $= -5$

$As = +5$

Today, the land surface and most water bodies exhibit oxidising conditions due to the abundance of oxygen both in the atmosphere and dissolved in water. They are *aerobic*. However, in some aqueous environments into which currents do not transport oxygen, as in stagnant lakes and in some groundwater (Section 3.2), conditions can become *anaerobic* and reducing. Oxidation reactions used by **aerobic bacteria** consume available oxygen to break down dead organic matter and, as a result, may eventually create oxygen-free conditions. Reducing conditions then develop, often to be colonised by **anaerobic bacteria** that use different kinds of reducing reactions in their metabolism. Chapter 3 considers these modern conditions in more detail in relation to arsenic and iron(III).

The Earth's surface environments were not always oxidising. The first primitive single-celled life forms emerged about 4 billion years ago, when reducing conditions prevailed everywhere. Those elements that can have several oxidation states would have been in less-oxidised states than those that prevail today. Of the transition elements, iron is by far the most common and it would have been in its iron(II) state. Iron(II) (i.e. Fe^{2+}) ions are soluble in water, whereas those of iron(III) (Fe^{3+}) are far less so.

As today, the most important Earth process would have been the generation of oceanic crust by continual outpouring of basaltic magma from the mantle. Hot and in contact with water, common iron-rich minerals in basalt would have decomposed to release Fe^{2+} ions. In modern, oxygenated ocean water, iron(II) is quickly oxidised by losing an electron to oxygen to form iron(III), which in turn reacts with water to form insoluble **iron(III) hydroxide**.

$$4Fe^{2+}(aq) + 6H_2O(l) + O_2(aq) = 4FeOOH(s) + 8H^+ \qquad (2.5)$$

Note: To chemists, the familiar formula for iron(III) hydroxide is $Fe(OH)_3$. Under natural conditions this is quickly transformed to a mineral known as *goethite*, which is an *oxy-hydroxide* whose formula is FeOOH. *We use this formula throughout because it reflects reality, calling it 'iron(III) hydroxide' for simplicity.*

On the oxygen-free early Earth, iron(II) could remain in solution as the Fe^{2+} ion in seawater. So too could reduced ions of other transition metals, particularly nickel and cobalt that are enriched relative to most other rare elements in ocean-floor basalt. Lower oxidation states of other elements induced them to be *less* soluble than they are now. Sulfur would dominantly have existed in its −2 oxidation state, encouraging the formation of H_2S rather than sulfate ions (Box 2.1). Reactions between H_2S and transition-metal ions would have precipitated metal sulfides. This low oxidation state in seawater formed the chemical conditions for the emergence and early evolution of life, which would have exploited and adapted to that aqueous chemistry.

hydrogen sulphide

Some of the most complex organic compounds in modern life-forms are proteins. Many protein structures include traces of iron, nickel, cobalt and other transition metals in combination with sulfur (Figure 2.4). Some authorities have taken this as evidence for the origin of life and its chemical 'building blocks' near to abundant sources of soluble iron, nickel and cobalt, particularly around springs that issued from the ocean floor (Figure 2.5). There, seawater circulated through hot oceanic crust, altering it and releasing ions of iron, nickel and cobalt that were soluble in oxygen-free seawater.

Some time before about 2.2 billion years ago, a group of bacteria (blue–green, or cyanobacteria) evolved photosynthesis, which emits oxygen as a waste product. Once oxygen gas appeared, it would have served to oxidise Fe(II) ions in aqueous solution (Equation 2.5). While entry of iron(II) into ocean water

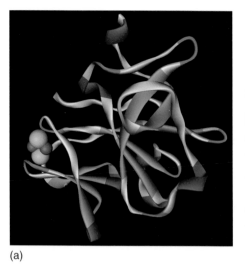

(a)   (b)

Figure 2.4   Molecular structures of possibly primitive proteins that incorporate transition-group metals and sulfur. (a) Rieske protein from *Thermus thermophilus*, showing the protein structure, iron (blue spheres) and sulfur (yellow spheres); (b) rubredoxin from *Pyrococcus furiosus* containing nickel (blue sphere). Both *Thermus thermophilus* and *Pyrococcus furiosus* are members of the Archaea domain that can survive in boiling water. Both Rieske and nickel-bearing proteins also occur in eukaryotes.

outweighed photosynthetic oxygen production, the atmosphere and hydrosphere would have remained reducing, except for those ecological niches where cyanobacteria released oxygen. All free oxygen would have entered iron(III) hydroxide deposited on the sea floor. In continental sedimentary rocks around 2.2 billion years old, geoscientists find ancient soils coloured red by insoluble iron(III) oxides and hydroxides, whereas older soils show no such coloration. Red soils formed by atmospheric weathering of the continental surface signify an atmosphere that contained free oxygen whose source could only have been oxygenated seawater. Thereafter, the Earth's biosphere became dominated by oxidising environments: the chemistry for life had shifted abruptly and decisively.

All members of the Eukarya domain of living things, of which plants and animals are multi-celled forms, require free oxygen for their metabolism. Eukaryote cells contain nuclei in which most of their genetic material is located, unlike single-celled prokaryotes – the Bacteria and Archaea domains – whose genetic material is not confined by a nuclear membrane. Bacteria and Archaea emerged, survived and evolved in a reducing chemical environment. The Eukarya exploited for the first time the biochemical power of oxidation reactions conferred by oxygen. Around 2.2 billion years ago, life was presented with an almost pervasive oxidising environment. This would have probably encouraged the expansion of the Eukarya, but would have been near-pervasively toxic for the Archaea and many Bacteria. This had three fundamental consequences for life on Earth.

Figure 2.5   Hot water gushing from modern ocean-floor basalt. Its content of dissolved metal ions reacts with hydrogen sulfide produced by primitive bacteria to precipitate metal sulfides. This process generates the dark cloud of fine-grained precipitates, from which such springs get their colloquial name: 'black smokers'.

1   Ecological niches for anaerobic Archaea and Bacteria were dramatically reduced to a few environments that were cut off from oxygen, which is toxic for most of these simple organisms.

2   Much of the world became available to oxygen-dependent Eukarya, of which we are a highly evolved member. It is worth noting that oxygen is toxic at the cell level even for Eukarya that use it in their metabolism. That Eukarya survived is due to their deployment of a range of anti-oxidant proteins, many of which incorporate iron and other transition metals. Anti-oxidant structures are similar to proteins used by Archaea that live in extreme conditions, such as hot springs, and help repair damage caused by the heat. Those vital necessities for the earliest life forms seem to have been 're-branded' by their eukaryote descendants in order to survive a different threat.

■   What do you think the third fundamental transformation would have been?

▨   Elements capable of existing in several oxidation states would have entered those states compatible with oxidising conditions. That is, electron donors (e.g. metals) would have become increasingly positive and electron acceptors increasingly negative.

3   Essential transition metals, such as iron, nickel and cobalt, became less abundant in water, because their more oxidised ions are far less soluble than those stable under reducing conditions. On the other hand, some elements more easily entered solution as ions, an example being sulfur in its +6 state as sulfate ions (SO_4^{2-}), together with the transition metals copper and zinc. Their concentration in seawater increased and made them newly available to cell processes, to confer potential advantages or disadvantages.

Since life had evolved in predominantly reducing conditions for around 1.8 billion years prior to that fateful event, thereafter cell processes had to adapt to increased concentrations of some ions and reduced availability of others.

Eukaryote cell processes evolved chemically over the last 2.2 billion years, establishing narrow tolerances to some elements and toxic response to others. Good examples of Eukarya exploiting the opportunities presented to them by increased oxidation are the biological roles played by copper and zinc. Under earlier reducing conditions, those metals were largely taken up by sulfide minerals, but their more oxidised ions are more soluble. They are now central to a range of proteins used by Eukarya, such as copper in the 'action' hormone adrenaline and in melatonin that helps stabilise biological rhythms. Zinc occurs in the steroids that are involved in sexual functions, which are unique to the Eukarya. Similarly, selenium (with sulfur in Group VI (or 16) of the Periodic Table) that was previously taken up by selenide minerals is now an essential trace element.

Some metals, such as cadmium (Cd), lead (Pb) and mercury (Hg) that enter insoluble sulfides under reducing conditions, seem never to have had a biological role once they appeared as dissolved ions in oxidising environments. Yet, they can cross cell membranes to interfere with chemical processes within cells: they constitute 'poisons'. To some extent, evolution has produced mechanisms whereby small amounts of Cd, Pb and Hg can be pumped out again. Higher concentrations of these elements result in their long-term residence within the cell, which eventually kill it. The probable response of the Eukarya to increased abundances of newly soluble ions under oxidising conditions since 2.2 billion years ago can be summarised as follows:

New ion → poison → protective detoxification → useful properties in cell processes → essential incorporation into cells

Copper and zinc are examples of 'new ions' that have passed through all these stages, whereas cadmium, lead and mercury are still poisons warded off by limited protective detoxification. We shall come to arsenic in a little more detail, shortly.

Evolutionary adaptation of Eukarya to the shift to an oxidising environment was not cut and dried, as the following biochemical conflict between zinc and iron shows. Zinc and iron(II) compete for positions in organic molecules because of their similar ionic size. Consequently, the zinc supplements that men especially are encouraged to take, partly for their supposed efficacy in promoting sexual potency, can be a threat to earlier, more fundamental cell processes that use the properties of iron(II). Excessive zinc consumption results in anaemia (Table 2.1) by disrupting iron(II)-based haemoglobin in red blood cells. As we all know, anaemia causes fatigue, so it is wise to go easy on the mineral supplement pills!

2.2.1 The biological chemistry of arsenic

Arsenic is like a metal, being shiny, soft and malleable, and electrically conductive. But it also has properties associated with non-metals, being in Group V (or Group 15) of the Periodic Table (Figure 2.3) below nitrogen and phosphorus and above antimony and bismuth. Arsenic is a *semi-metal*. It has an unusually large range of oxidation states, commonly −3, +3 and +5 (Box 2.1, Question 2.3). Under natural conditions, arsenic comes into contact with organisms in aqueous solution as arsenite ions (AsO_3^{3-}) in its +3 state and arsenate ions (AsO_4^{3-}) in its +5 state. *Throughout Topic 3, whenever we refer to 'arsenic' in well water you can assume that it means both these ions in aqueous solution, which we do not distinguish for simplicity.* Negatively charged arsenite and arsenate ions can adhere tightly to the surfaces of some common minerals whose molecular structure produces a positive charge excess on the outer parts of their molecules (Section 3.3). Arsine (AsH_3) gas is by far the most toxic form of arsenic, followed by dissolved arsenite and then arsenate compounds. The elemental form of arsenic is the least toxic, though fatal if taken in even small quantities.

The bulk of arsenic in crustal rocks resides in sulfide minerals, such as **pyrite** (FeS_2), in which it can replace sulfur ions. Arsenic plays virtually no role in the dominant silicates of the Earth's crust and mantle. It is one of the less abundant elements in rocks of the continental crust (Figure 2.6).

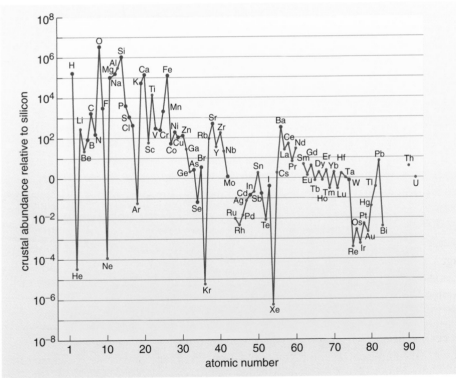

Figure 2.6   Plot of the abundances of elements in the Earth's crust, relative to the abundance of silicon (set arbitrarily at 10^6 or 1 million), against their atomic numbers. Elements that play some role in living organisms are highlighted by red dots. Note: an element shown with an abundance of 10^4 is 100 times less abundant than silicon 10^6. This kind of plot clearly separates elements with a huge range of true abundances by mass, without making the vertical scale astronomically high.

■ Which of the other elements regarded as essential or useful in living processes (Table 2.2) are less abundant than arsenic?

▨ Only selenium, molybdenum, cadmium, tungsten, antimony and iodine occur at lower abundances.

The average concentration of arsenic in the continental crust is about 1.5 parts per million (ppm) by mass (i.e. 1.5 mg kg^{-1}), occurring mainly in sulfide minerals. It is the 51st most common element. In natural waters, concentrations are usually well below 10 parts per billion by volume (ppbv) (10 micrograms per litre or 10 μg l^{-1}), the WHO recommended maximum for safe drinking water.

■   Under the oxidising conditions of the modern Earth's surface, in which oxidation state would you expect to find arsenic dissolved in water?

▨   Oxidising conditions would favour the +3 and +5 oxidation states.

Arsenic in modern water will occur mainly as the arsenite and arsenate ions. Arsenic in the −3 oxidation state is less soluble than arsenic in the +3 or +5 oxidation states.

■   Do you think arsenic would have been present dissolved in water before 2.2 billion years ago?

▨   Under reducing conditions, the oxidised +3 and +5 states would be uncommon, and dissolved arsenic much less abundant than now.

So, arsenic has all the attributes of an element which first came into contact with cells in significant amounts after the Earth's surface became dominated by oxidising conditions. Arsenic's lower crustal abundance than those of most elements that play any positive biological role implies that it would be less likely to come into contact with organisms than many other elements. It is a prime candidate for having retained potentially poisonous effects by virtue of its rarity.

You may be surprised to learn how many uses this widely feared element has. Between 75 000 tonnes and 100 000 tonnes of arsenic are produced commercially each year as by-products of the mining of several metals, including gold. Perhaps the most astonishing of all arsenic's uses is in growth promoters for pigs and poultry, albeit in very small amounts. Arsenic's potent toxicity to all life forms when it occurs at high concentrations finds many uses as a rodenticide, and in wood preservatives, tanning and taxidermy. Arsenic in British groundwater is strongly correlated with proximity to graveyards, because arsenic compounds are used in embalming. 'Agent Blue', used in the US defoliation campaign during the Vietnam War, is dimethylarsinic acid. Some arsenic compounds, such as gallium arsenide, generate light when exposed to longwave infrared radiation, and are used in thermal-imaging cameras. Historically, elemental arsenic has been used medicinally, such as in arsenic-rich amulets worn as a protection against plagues in medieval times. Until 1909 it was the principal drug used to treat syphilis. Paul Ehrlich's famous 'magic bullet' for the treatment of syphilis incorporated arsenic compounds. A popular cure-all in Victorian times was Dr Fowler's Solution (potassium arsenate), whose most famous user was Charles Dickens. Arsenic has recently been found to be an effective treatment for pancreatic cancer and some forms of leukaemia. These drugs selectively encourage programmed death (*apoptosis*) of cancerous cells, which is the hallmark of many kinds of chemotherapy. Many other uses and abuses are described by Andrew Meharg in *Venomous Earth* (2005).

Once ingested, arsenic rapidly combines with haemoglobin and pervades the body through blood circulation. It accumulates in organs and tissue by substitution for phosphorus, for example in adenosine triphosphate (ATP), which plays a fundamental role in metabolism. As and P are in the same group of the Periodic Table (Figure 2.3). Within 24 hours, arsenic redistributes itself to the skin, liver, kidney, spleen, lungs and gastro-intestinal tract, with lesser accumulation in muscle, nerve and brain tissues.

Symptoms of *acute* arsenic poisoning by high accidental or deliberate doses begin with headaches, confusion and drowsiness. As the poisoning develops, the breath may smell like garlic and the fingernails change colour. Later symptoms include diarrhoea, vomiting, blood in the urine, cramping muscles, hair loss, stomach pain and convulsions. The final result of acute arsenic poisoning is coma followed by death. That was the fate of the Outhwaite family (Chapter 1). Recognised at an early stage, acute arsenic poisoning can be treated by chelation therapy. The treatment involves administering compounds that incorporate arsenic more readily than do those involved in cell biochemistry, and which can be expelled from the cell so that the arsenic is excreted rapidly. However, the treatment is lengthy and cannot reverse the damage already done.

The symptoms of *chronic* arsenic poisoning develop through gradual build-up of arsenic in the system from repeated small doses, such as from drinking arsenic-contaminated water. The general term for the effects is **arsenicosis.** The most obvious early signs are horny skin lesions (keratoses) on the hands and feet (Figure 2.7a and b). The keratoses often develop gangrene infections. The first signs of arsenic poisoning noticed in Bangladeshis were dark blotches that were distributed evenly across the body (Figure 2.7c) (the 'black rain' mentioned in *Perfectly Poisoned*), which are difficult to distinguish from birthmarks, pigmented moles (both of which may eventually become cancerous) or even freckles. Arsenic is now known to cause cancers of the lung, liver, kidney and bladder, but these cancers have other causes as well, and a link to arsenic is not immediately obvious. Its effect on the nervous system causes

Figure 2.7 Early signs of chronic arsenic poisoning: (a) and (b) skin lesions or keratoses; (c) skin discoloration or dyspigmentation.

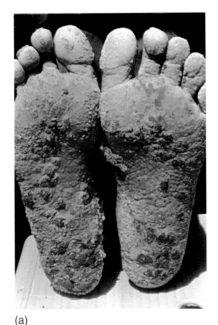

(a)

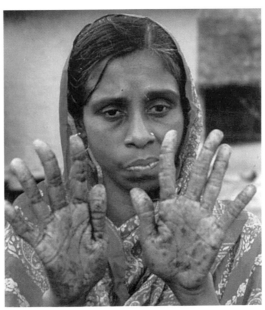

(b)

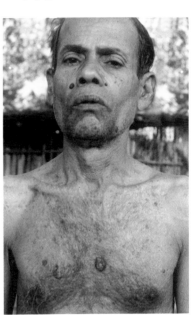

(c)

numbness (a reason why arsenicosis can be mistaken for leprosy and be stigmatised) and eventually muscular atrophy, paralysis and loss of coordination. Arsenic has recently been implicated in high incidences of atherosclerosis ('hardening of the arteries') and a form of diabetes.

The early symptoms of chronic arsenic poisoning were first diagnosed in adjoining West Bengal in India during the early 1980s, then in Bangladesh in the mid 1990s. Later, abnormally high incidences of a variety of cancers began to emerge. Exactly why arsenic causes cancers is not certain. It is believed to act indirectly on DNA, possibly by interfering with the suppression of powerfully oxidising hydroxyl ions and hydrogen peroxide by anti-oxidant enzymes. Another possibility is that arsenic inhibits the transcription of a gene known as hTERT that controls the generation of the enzyme telomerase. This enzyme protects the ends of chromosomes (*telomeres*) from end-to-end fusion, a known cause of genetic instability. Such a malformation can also lead to cell death (apoptosis), thereby explaining the paradox of arsenic compounds acting as both carcinogens and anti-cancer agents.

2.3 Evaluating the risk from waterborne arsenic

R

Arsenic clearly poses a hazard; indeed, it has entered many cultures as the archetypical instrument of stealthy murder: it adds no taste to food or drink. As a drinking-water contaminant its action is just as insidious. While early signs of chronic arsenic poisoning are distinctive (Figure 2.7), many of its later and eventually fatal effects from cancers have many other possible causes. So the ultimate consequences of arsenic contamination of water supplies are hard to separate from those of other hazards. Lung cancer is a case in point. Although arsenic ingested in drinking water can produce lung cancer, so too can smoking, irradiation and inhalation of various irritant dusts. Similarly, skin cancers also result from overexposure to ultraviolet wavelengths in sunlight. Somehow, the third aspect of risk – exposure – has to be evaluated in relation to the other two, i.e. hazard and consequences. Exposure cannot be estimated by experimental means using laboratory animal subjects, as the only relevant subjects are humans themselves.

Health problems that arise from occupational exposure to very high arsenic levels have been extensively studied, for instance among workers employed in metal mines and smelters, in vineyards where arsenic compounds are used as fungicides and, more recently, in the manufacture of semiconductors. It is now common practice to monitor levels of arsenic in the hair and urine of people exposed to it in industry. There are, however, few studies that use medical records of endemic illnesses and death attributed to arsenic in drinking water, which would help establish the harmful range on a dose–response curve (Figure 2.2).

In northern Chile between 1955 and 1969, arsenic content of the drinking water supply for 400 000 people in the city of Antofagasta reached extremely high levels because it was derived from a source contaminated by effluent from mines. Studies there showed that seven or eight people in every 100 who drank water containing 500 µg l^{-1} of arsenic over 14 years probably died from internal cancers attributable to arsenic.

■   Do you think the study in Antofagasta is helpful in establishing risk from exposure to arsenic elsewhere?

▨   This study is not particularly helpful as the exposure was only to one extremely high concentration in the citywide supply. That would give only one point in establishing a dose–response relationship. Moreover, the information on ill health is too general to establish that aspect of risk for a range of cancers and contains no information on skin conditions, which are the first symptoms to appear.

To give you a better idea of the risk from waterborne arsenic, Sections 2.3.1 and 2.3.2 examine data from India and Taiwan. The first study is from a small part of West Bengal, India, that adjoins western Bangladesh. People in both areas have drunk arsenic-contaminated well water from similar sources since the 1970s. The study centred on the initial, visible signs of arsenic-related ailments: keratoses and abnormal pigmentation of the skin. The second study is of people from parts of Taiwan who have used water from arsenic-contaminated springs and wells for more than 100 years. In Taiwan, various cancers are endemic in the population, as well as the typical skin discoloration and keratoses. So the Taiwanese study gives some indication of how arsenic-related ill health in Bangladesh might develop, should adequate remedial measures not be deployed there.

2.3.1 West Bengal case study

Table 2.3 shows data for the number of people examined in the West Bengal study area, according to their exposure to different arsenic concentrations in drinking water. Tables 2.4 and 2.5 show the proportion of people who have the typical early signs of chronic arsenic poisoning. The survey also divided people according to their gender and age, so you will be able to evaluate several aspects of the risk associated from living in an area of arsenic contamination.

The survey involved over 7500 individuals who have been exposed to arsenic in eight ranges of concentration, from below the locally recommended maximum of 50 µg l^{-1} to very high concentrations (Table 2.3). Age ranges are from the under-10s to the 60s and over, in 10-year groups, which should help you to evaluate roughly how long it takes for sufficient arsenic to accumulate to give the typical outward signs of chronic poisoning. There may also be some relationship with gender. The data in each cell for specific age range, gender and range of arsenic concentrations in Tables 2.4 and 2.5 show the percentage of people who are affected (the incidence), with the actual numbers in brackets. For example, the cell for females aged 0 to 9 years exposed to water containing between 350 µg l^{-1} and 499 µg l^{-1} arsenic (highlighted) shows 50 individuals in Table 2.3, of whom one shows skin keratoses – an incidence of 2.0% in Table 2.4. In Table 2.5, for the same group, six individuals or 12.0% show abnormal skin pigmentation. For each gender and each ailment, the total incidence and number of affected individuals are given for each concentration range, irrespective of age. The different numbers in each age/concentration group bias those figures, and an allowance for that is made in the 'age-adjusted' row in Tables 2.4 and 2.5. The 'age-adjusted' incidence (given as a percentage) is a general measure of risk to the whole population. The right-hand columns for a particular age group show the number and percentage who are affected by arsenic-related symptoms.

Table 2.3 Number of people by gender and age who drink well water with different ranges of arsenic concentration in part of West Bengal, India.

Arsenic concentration /µg 1^{-1}	<50	50–99	100–149	150–199	200–349	350–499	500–799	>800	Total examined
females, ages									
≤9	194	31	53	23	84	50	75	26	536
10–19	400	74	58	54	117	57	65	26	851
20–29	577	102	99	74	135	63	83	24	1157
30–39	308	79	48	46	79	40	44	15	659
40–49	175	33	23	27	36	21	28	10	353
50–59	157	38	23	18	27	18	30	11	322
≥60	97	29	9	17	27	20	10	6	215
all ages	1908	386	313	259	505	269	335	118	4093
males, ages									
≤9	220	64	65	27	77	51	81	28	613
10–19	330	73	49	56	96	51	64	29	748
20–29	356	79	56	52	79	43	59	25	749
30–39	246	63	38	40	75	44	53	18	577
40–49	160	43	29	24	53	22	25	12	368
50–59	121	29	17	15	35	19	23	11	270
≥60	126	34	20	21	27	16	15	6	265
all ages	1559	385	274	235	442	246	320	129	3590

Table 2.4 Incidence per hundred (i.e. percentage) and number (in brackets) of people by gender and age who show skin keratoses by different ranges of arsenic concentration in the water that they drink.

Arsenic concentration /µg 1^{-1}	<50	50–99	100–149	150–199	200–349	350–499	500–799	>800	Total examined
females, ages									
≤9	0.0(0)	0.0(0)	0.0(0)	0.0(0)	0.0(0)	2.0(1)	0.0(0)	0.0(0)	0.2(1)
10–19	0.0(0)	0.0(0)	0.0(0)	1.9(1)	2.6(3)	0.0(0)	3.1(2)	11.5(3)	1.0(9)
20–29	0.0(0)	0.0(0)	1.0(1)	1.4(1)	1.5(2)	3.2(2)	0.0(0)	4.2(1)	0.6(7)
30–39	0.0(0)	2.5(2)	0.0(0)	2.2(1)	2.5(2)	2.5(1)	4.6(2)	0.0(0)	1.2(8)
40–49	0.0(0)	0.0(0)	0.0(0)	0.0(0)	5.6(2)	9.5(2)	10.7(3)	10.0(1)	2.3(8)
50–59	0.0(0)	0.0(0)	4.4(1)	11.1(2)	0.0(0)	0.0(0)	10.0(3)	27.3(3)	2.8(9)
≥60	0.0(0)	0.0(0)	11.1(1)	5.9(1)	3.7(1)	5.0(1)	0.0(0)	33.3(2)	2.8(6)
all ages	0.0(0)	0.5(2)	1.0(3)	2.3(6)	2.0(10)	2.6(7)	3.0(10)	8.5(10)	1.2(48)
age-adjusted*	0.0	0.4	1.2	2.3	2.0	2.7	3.1	8.3	1.2

Arsenic concentration /μg 1^{-1}	<50	50–99	100–149	150–199	200–349	350–499	500–799	>800	Total examined
males, ages									
≤9	0.0(0)	0.0(0)	0.0(0)	3.7(1)	1.3(1)	2.0(1)	0.0(0)	0.0(0)	0.5(3)
10–19	0.3(1)	0.0(0)	0.0(0)	1.8(1)	5.2(5)	3.9(2)	3.1(2)	6.9(2)	1.7(13)
20–29	0.0(0)	0.0(0)	1.8(1)	3.8(2)	5.1(4)	7.0(3)	10.2(6)	20.0(5)	2.8(21)
30–39	0.4(1)	3.7(2)	2.6(1)	7.5(3)	6.7(5)	15.9(7)	18.9(10)	22.2(4)	5.7(33)
40–49	0.0(0)	4.7(2)	0.0(0)	8.3(2)	5.7(3)	27.3(6)	12.0(3)	8.3(1)	4.6(17)
50–59	0.8(1)	6.9(2)	5.9(1)	6.7(1)	8.6(3)	15.8(3)	13.0(3)	9.1(1)	5.6(15)
≥60	0.8(1)	0.0(0)	5.0(1)	4.8(1)	3.7(1)	0.0(0)	13.3(2)	0.0(0)	2.3(6)
all ages	0.3(4)	1.6(6)	1.5(4)	4.7(11)	5.0(22)	8.9(22)	8.1(26)	10.1(13)	3.0(108)
age-adjusted*	0.2	1.5	1.6	4.7	4.9	9.0	8.9	10.7	3.0

* i.e. adjusted for the different numbers of people in the age groups.

Table 2.5 Incidence per hundred (i.e. percentage) and number (in brackets) of people by gender and age who show abnormal skin pigmentation by different ranges of arsenic concentration in the water that they drink.

Arsenic concentration /μg 1^{-1}	<50	50–99	100–149	150–199	200–349	350–499	500–799	>800	Total examined
females, ages									
≤9	0.0(0)	0.0(0)	1.9(1)	0.0(0)	2.4(2)	12.0(6)	0.0(0)	0.0(0)	1.7(9)
10–19	0.0(0)	0.0(0)	1.7(1)	5.6(3)	7.7(9)	1.8(1)	3.1(2)	11.5(3)	2.2(19)
20–29	0.0(0)	0.0(0)	1.0(1)	4.0(3)	4.4(6)	11.1(7)	6.0(5)	8.3(2)	2.1(24)
30–39	0.0(0)	1.3(1)	12.5(6)	6.5(3)	8.9(7)	12.5(5)	0.0(0)	6.7(1)	3.5(23)
40–49	1.4(2)	0.0(0)	13.0(3)	3.7(1)	16.7(6)	14.3(3)	17.9(5)	20.0(2)	6.2(22)
50–59	1.9(3)	2.6(1)	13.0(3)	11.1(2)	0.0(0)	5.6(1)	16.7(5)	27.3(3)	5.6(18)
≥60	0.0(0)	6.9(2)	11.1(1)	11.8(2)	7.4(2)	15.0(3)	0.0(0)	33.3(2)	5.6(12)
all ages	0.3(5)	1.0(4)	5.1(16)	5.4(14)	6.3(32)	9.7(26)	5.1(17)	11.0(13)	3.1(127)
age-adjusted*	0.3	0.8	5.7	5.1	6.5	9.5	5.3	11.5	3.1
males, ages									
≤9	0.0(0)	0.0(0)	4.6(3)	3.7(1)	3.9(3)	5.9(3)	0.0(0)	7.1(2)	2.0(12)
10–19	0.0(0)	2.7(2)	2.0(1)	3.6(2)	9.4(9)	11.8(6)	3.1(2)	13.8(4)	3.5(26)
20–29	0.8(3)	1.3(1)	12.5(7)	11.5(6)	17.7(14)	14.0(6)	13.6(8)	36.0(9)	7.2(54)
30–39	0.4(1)	3.2(2)	15.8(6)	12.5(5)	13.3(10)	22.7(10)	22.6(12)	33.3(6)	9.0(52)
40–49	0.0(0)	11.6(5)	10.3(3)	8.3(2)	13.2(7)	40.9(9)	16.0(4)	25.0(3)	9.0(33)
50–59	2.5(3)	6.9(2)	5.9(1)	6.7(1)	28.6(10)	15.8(3)	39.1(9)	45.5(5)	2.6(34)
≥60	0.0(0)	2.9(1)	45.0(9)	9.5(2)	18.5(5)	6.3(1)	33.3(5)	0.0(0)	8.7(23)
all ages	0.5(7)	3.4(13)	11.0(30)	8.1(19)	13.2(58)	15.5(38)	12.5(40)	22.5(29)	6.5(234)
age-adjusted*	0.4	3.2	11.0	7.8	13.1	15.7	13.8	22.7	6.4

* i.e. adjusted for the different numbers of people in the age groups.

Question 2.4

From the data in Tables 2.4 and 2.5, answer the following. (a) Can a concentration of 50 μg l⁻¹ (the maximum recommended concentration adopted by the Bangladesh Government) or less be regarded as 'safe'? (b) Is it possible to judge the minimum period that it takes for arsenic-related health problems to appear, and if so what is the likely length of exposure involved? (c) Are there any noticeable differences between male and female susceptibility to skin keratoses and abnormal skin pigmentation? If so, think of a possible explanation and how you might test that hypothesis. *Hint*: think of the probable lifestyle of each gender.

Figure 2.8 shows the incidence of keratosis and **hyperpigmentation** as histograms according to the arsenic concentration in drinking water. The differences between genders show up very clearly. Another genetic aspect of arsenic's toxicity emerged from studies in 2005 at the University of Arizona, USA, which concentrated on a gene (CYT19) that codes for enzymes involved in the metabolism of arsenic. The study shows that, depending on variations in the gene, some children are more genetically susceptible to arsenic than other individuals who are able to tolerate higher amounts of arsenic without harm to their health. These findings, if confirmed, further complicate the assessment of risk in populations exposed to arsenic.

Figure 2.8 Age-adjusted incidences (%) in males and females in West Bengal for skin keratoses and abnormal pigmentation shown as histograms against arsenic concentration ranges.

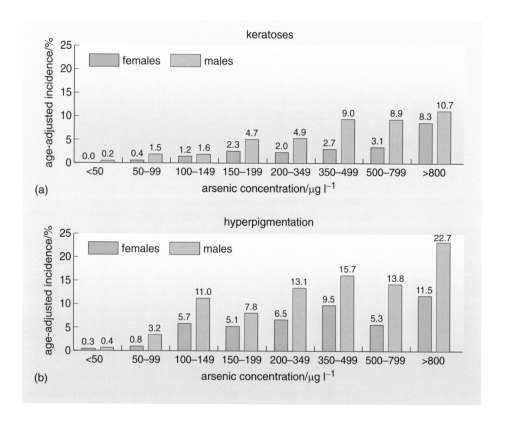

■ Are the data in Figure 2.8 useful in assessing a dose–response curve for arsenic?

■ They do show that incidence of the two conditions rises with the degree of exposure to arsenic contamination. So they express increasing risk of contracting skin keratoses and abnormal pigmentation. But neither condition is fatal; therefore, risk to life is not shown. They relate to points F to G on Figure 2.2.

Internal cancers develop with prolonged arsenic exposure and are probably at the earliest stages in West Bengal and Bangladesh. Nevertheless, the data in Tables 2.4 and 2.5 are useful in assessing arsenic levels that lead to highly disfiguring skin problems, which are probably precursors to the onset of potentially fatal diseases.

2.3.2 Taiwan case study

Figure 2.9 shows mortality data from four types of cancer that have been estimated for average arsenic concentrations in some Taiwanese well water. The averages are for three ranges of arsenic contamination (<300 μg l^{-1}, 300–600 μg l^{-1}, >600 μg l^{-1}) in part of Taiwan that has concentrations above the WHO recommended maximum (0.01 mg l^{-1}, or 10 μg l^{-1} in Table 2.1). The mortalities at 0 μg l^{-1} represent the average mortality rate for Taiwan as a whole.

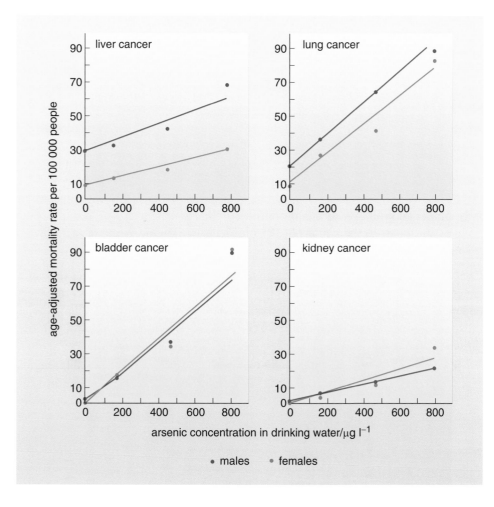

Figure 2.9 Age-adjusted mortality rates in males and females in Taiwan for various cancers plotted against arsenic concentration in drinking water (the arsenic concentrations are for the average in each range).

Question 2.5

Describe the way in which incidences of conditions shown by Figures 2.8 and 2.9 vary according to arsenic concentrations. Would you be able to predict the number of people likely to be adversely affected from prolonged exposure to water with particular concentrations (i.e. the consequences)?

2.3.3 Risk and exposure

The two case studies should have shown you that evaluating the dose and response for exposure to arsenic in drinking water is complicated by two factors.

1   There is a time lag between the start of exposure and the appearance of adverse consequences. For skin conditions, this may be of the order of 10 years and for internal cancers somewhat longer.

2   There are many potential consequences, for which the relationship to dose varies.

R   Despite the complications, the overall risk of arsenic concentrations in drinking water is clearly severe. Around 21 million people in Bangladesh are exposed to arsenic concentrations of 50 μg l^{-1} or more. Some epidemiologists estimate that 1.3% (~300 000) of the population are likely to die from arsenic-induced cancers if remedial measures are not introduced soon. Many may already face that fate, in spite of rapid action. Because of the linear relationship between dose and incidence of cancers in Taiwan (Figure 2.9), those drinking higher levels face higher risks. For instance, there is a considerably higher probability of dying from bladder cancer with long-term exposure to more than 600 μg l^{-1} than among the Taiwanese population as a whole.

Alarmingly, studies published in 2004 on the effects of arsenic on cell cultures suggest that levels up to 20 times *lower* than the WHO-recommended maximum level in water (10 μg l^{-1}) act as an endocrine inhibitor. Endocrine-disrupting chemicals disturb hormone signalling and regulation in the body, and are implicated in several forms of cancer, heart disease, diabetes, and reproductive or developmental problems. If this is confirmed, then arsenic may well be an unavoidable contributor to many health problems worldwide, because such low levels in water are the norm.

Chapter 3 concentrates on why arsenic has naturally entered well water in Bangladesh. Without a clear idea of the causes, then assessing the risks of endemic illness in Bangladesh and other areas of the world, and developing the means of either removing arsenic from the water or finding safe sources, will be difficult.

Summary of Chapter 2

1   All organisms are exposed to the 91 naturally occurring elements, of which between 20 and 32 play a role in metabolism. For most of these essential elements, inadequate exposure results in symptoms of deficiency; a higher range of ingested concentrations promotes health; excessive exposure results in symptoms that reflect poisoning. These ranges can be expressed by a dose–response relationship.

2   The availability of elements as water-soluble ions partly depends on their oxidation state, but more importantly in nature it depends on the stability of minerals that can contain them under oxidising and reducing conditions. Even the action of different micro-organisms can play a role by changing chemical conditions.

3   Some of our requirements for essential elements stem from the reducing chemical environment in which life appeared and evolved from 2.2 billion years ago, whereas other elements entered cell processes after conditions became oxidising, enabling them to exist in aqueous solution and find a metabolic role.

4   Although very low levels of arsenic may have some physiological function, most concentrations have a poisoning effect, expressed in different ways by long-term (chronic) exposure to low levels or single very high doses (acute).

5   Arsenic is one element to which biological evolution has not adjusted after it became more readily soluble once the surface environment became oxidising, and so it acts as a poison. Chronic poisoning first gives the symptoms of arsenicosis, which are spots of discoloured skin and wart-like skin lesions. Later symptoms include a variety of cancers.

6   Risk from poisonous chemicals is expressed by hazard, exposure and consequences. Data from West Bengal show that symptoms of arsenicosis appear within 10 years of the start of continuous exposure to arsenic above 50 μg l^{-1} in drinking water. Taiwanese data for various cancers show that the likelihood of an early death from these conditions increases linearly with the arsenic concentration in drinking water. In both manifestations of chronic arsenic poisoning, there are differences between males and females, with females being less likely to show symptoms.

Chapter 3

Geological processes and groundwater

Millions of wells in Bangladesh supply water from geologically young sediments that lie beneath the flood plains and deltas of the country's large rivers. The wells penetrate to a few hundred metres into mainly sands and gravels. These materials have not been cemented to form sedimentary rock: they are *unconsolidated*. The **groundwater** that they contain accumulates as part of the **water cycle** when rainfall and surface flow seep downwards through the sediments deposited by rivers. Groundwater is the proportion of this infiltration that becomes stored in sediments at depths of more than a few metres below the surface. Close to the surface, water in sediments or soil is prone to evaporation especially where solar heating is intense. So, to become stored as groundwater it needs to pass downwards fairly quickly. The proportion of water that enters subsurface storage depends on several factors:

- the amount of water present at the surface
- surface temperature
- how free-flowing the upper layers of soil are
- the amount of vegetation
- the flow speed of water across the surface, which in turn depends on the topographic slope.

Vegetation plays a dual role. It intercepts rainfall, which increases the chance of evaporation. Plants also use soil moisture and return a proportion back to the atmosphere by transpiration through pores (stomata) in their leaves. Vegetation also helps infiltration proceed more efficiently, partly by slowing down surface water flow and partly by preventing heavy rain battering the soil surface to an almost 'leak-proof' layer, which is not dissimilar to the way in which trampling humans at a rainy music festival create their own swamp.

Bangladesh is well endowed with groundwater. The monsoon generally ensures abundant rainfall through June to September. River flow is also supplemented by snow melting in the Himalaya. Surface slopes in most of the country are very gentle, so a high proportion of slow surface flow easily enters sediments on the plains to become groundwater. Intensive agriculture can increase infiltration as a result of ploughing and the seasonal flooding of rice fields.

Sediment that is saturated with groundwater lies at some depth below the surface. Pore spaces in near-surface materials, though often damp, contain air. The boundary between the **zone of aeration** and the **zone of saturation** is a surface known as the **water table**, whose depth varies. Beneath standing water, swamps and flowing rivers the water table coincides with the surface, but everywhere else it is hidden. When wells are not in use, water levels in them indicate the depth to the local water table. Where there are many wells it is possible to map accurately how that depth varies over large areas. Groundwater can flow if the water table slopes, but it flows a good deal more slowly than surface water because it has to move through constricted pores. It escapes where the water table meets the surface to add to river flow, either from springs or through river beds. There is generally a balance between infiltration and escape. Figure 3.1 summarises these concepts.

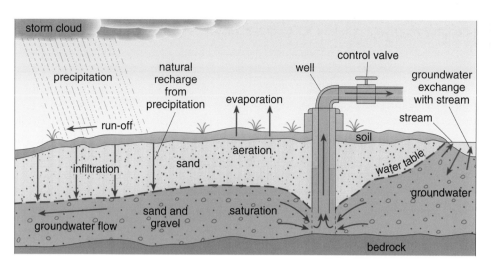

Figure 3.1   The underground component of the water cycle.

An important thing to remember from this introduction is that groundwater remains in contact with mineral grains in the sediments that contain it for longer than rainwater stays in aerated soil and much longer than surface water remains there. The longer that water and minerals remain in contact, the greater the chance of chemical interactions between them.

3.1   Groundwater in Bangladesh

Bangladesh is the world's most low-lying major country. It lies at the head of the Bay of Bengal on the great northern plains of the Indian Peninsula, between the Himalaya and the rolling hills of central India and Myanmar (Burma) (Figure 3.2). Apart from in the extreme southeast of the country, none of the land rises higher than 100 m and a great deal is only a few metres above sea level.

Most of the country is situated on the interfingering deltas of two great rivers (the Ganges and the Brahmaputra) that flow from the Himalaya, and a major tributary (the Meghna), which all discharge into the Bay of Bengal. The Ganges unites with the Brahmaputra (called the Jamuna in Bangladesh) and then joins the Meghna, which drains part of northeast India. Of a total area of 144 000 km², almost 10% of Bangladesh is taken up by river channels, and much of the country is routinely inundated during the summer monsoon season. Periodically, the 140 million Bangladeshi people suffer from climatic extremes. High river flows and sea-level surges driven by tropical cyclones in the Bay of Bengal cause catastrophic floods. The positive side of this threatening environment is that floods deposit fertile silts on which depends Bangladesh's high rural population density of, in places, up to one thousand people per square kilometre.

Since the Himalaya began to rise around 50 million years ago when the Indian subcontinent collided with Asia through plate tectonics, their growing elevation has encouraged the monsoon climate of South Asia. The monsoon precipitates up to 6 m in a few months in northeast India and over 1 m in the Himalayan foothills, together with thick snowfall in the Himalaya. Not surprisingly, the Ganges–Brahmaputra–Meghna river system comprises the third largest source of freshwater discharge to the world's oceans. Only the Amazon in Brazil and the Congo in Africa have larger discharges. The annual volume of flow just below the confluence of the Brahmaputra and Ganges is 795 billion cubic metres (7.95×10^{11} m³).

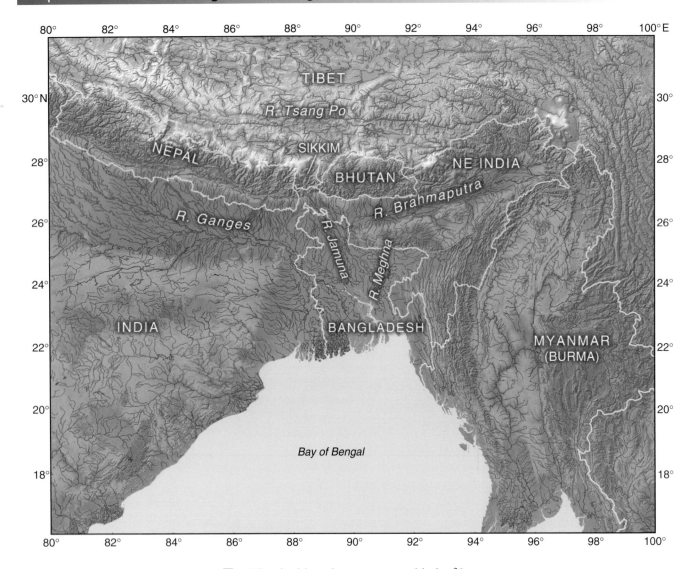

Figure 3.2   Regional topography of Bangladesh and surrounding countries. *Note*: there is a larger version of this image on the DVD-ROM. The Tsang Po and the Brahmaputra are the same river.

■ What is this volume expressed in km³?

▨ 1 km³ = 1000 m × 1000 m × 1000 m = 10^9 m³.

$$7.95 \times 10^{11}\,\text{m}^3 \text{ expressed in cubic kilometres} = \frac{7.95 \times 10^{11}\,\text{m}^3}{10^9\,\text{m}^3} = 7.95 \times 10^2\,\text{km}^3$$

This is an almost unimaginable volume, but the flow of Bangladesh's rivers is highly seasonal and spectacularly so. During monsoon floods, their combined discharge into the Bay of Bengal averages approximately 8.2×10^4 m³ s⁻¹. Since there are 8.64×10^4 s in a day ($60 \times 60 \times 24$), the daily flow is (8.2×10^4 m³ s⁻¹ × 8.64×10^4 s), which is 7.08×10^9 m³ or about 7 km³ per day. The solid load carried by rivers is also extremely high, supplying as much as 13 million tonnes per day of sediment to the onshore and offshore parts of their combined delta during the monsoon season.

■ What mass of sediment in kilograms is contained in 1 m³ of water at maximum flow rates?

▨ One tonne is 10^3 kg, so 13×10^6 t is the same as 1.3×10^{10} kg. When carried in 7.08×10^9 m³ of water this mass is equivalent to 1.84 kg m⁻³.

This is the highest sediment load carried by any large river in the world, so it is no surprise that there is plenty of sediment beneath Bangladesh to contain abundant groundwater.

The Ganges and the Brahmaputra rise in the Himalaya, which have high topographic elevation and steep slopes. There, *physical weathering* breaks down exposed hard rock to debris with a range of grain sizes (boulders to sand-sized particles) that becomes exposed to erosion by flowing water. The Himalaya also contain large mountain glaciers. Their awesome erosive power fills glacial ice with debris with an even greater range of grain sizes, from boulders down to ground-up mineral particles that can be as small as a few micrometres. At the snouts of glaciers, this jumble of broken material is dumped and exposed to erosion by glacial meltwater. Because the slopes down which the water flows are steep, Himalayan streams and rivers have very high energy until they emerge onto the flat plains of the northern Indian peninsula. All except the biggest boulders are transported, and even they become dislodged under gravity to fall into stream channels. In high-energy flowing water, the larger grains collide with boulders and are broken down into smaller sizes, thereby adding to the transported load. Figure 3.2 shows that the valleys of both rivers in the mountainous areas are narrow, and in the case of the Brahmaputra the narrow valley extends over almost its entire course. Opportunities for deposition, and hence reduction of the sediment load, are few in the mountains.

Under such extreme conditions, the slow process of *chemical weathering* has little chance to break down unstable silicate minerals to clay minerals and dissolved ions. This fundamental process in the rock cycle requires movement of rock and mineral fragments to stop, at least for a while (Section 3.2).

■ What happens to the rivers and their sediment loads when they reach the plains?

▨ The topographic gradient falls to almost zero, so the current speed drops and its energy decreases. Consequently, the larger transported grains are dumped to form unconsolidated sediments, while only the finer silts and smaller particles remain suspended in the rivers.

3.1.1 Why alluvium can contain abundant water supplies

The major rivers that cross the plains of the Ganges–Brahmaputra–Meghna delta system are highly seasonal in their flow rates, so the sediments that they deposit in one year can be picked up and transported again and again. Because of this, they become well sorted – the fine grains are winnowed out from the coarser ones and end up in the Bay of Bengal. Figure 3.3 compares the ways in which grains are arranged, and the distribution of grain sizes in well-sorted and poorly sorted sediments.

■ Which grain arrangement has the highest proportion of spaces to mineral grains?

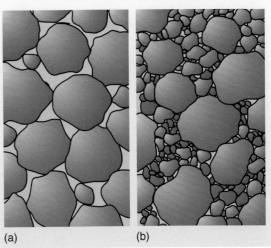

(a)   (b)

Figure 3.3   The structure of (a) well-sorted and (b) poorly sorted sediments.

■ The well-sorted arrangement. In the poorly sorted arrangement, the spaces between the large grains are partly filled by smaller grains.

The proportion of spaces to grains in a sediment controls its **porosity**, which is a measure of how much air or water it can contain. Sediments deposited in river systems as **alluvium** have a high potential water-storage capacity and are important sources of groundwater. However, to be useable the water must easily enter *and* be extracted from the sediment. This depends on how freely the water can flow through passages that connect the pore spaces.

■ Would you expect the rate of flow to increase or decrease as the passages become smaller?

■ The flow rate will decrease (in fact quite dramatically so) as the passages narrow.

You can easily observe this effect by pouring water onto dry, sandy soil and comparing it with water poured onto finer-grained clay soil. Water soaks in or infiltrates sandy soil almost immediately, whereas it ponds on the surface of clay soil.

■ Would you expect groundwater flow to be faster or slower in a poorly sorted sediment than in a well-sorted one?

■ Flow would be slower because the spaces between the larger grains are filled with smaller particles, giving narrower passages for flow.

To be a useful source of groundwater, sediment must combine the two attributes of high porosity and efficient movement of water between its pore spaces. Such a material is known as an **aquifer**. Most sands and gravels are good aquifers. The critical property is the ease of groundwater flow towards a well, both for its extraction and replenishment. Although fine-grained sediments (silts and clays) are often more porous than sands and gravels due to their internal structure, the speed of flow through them is slowed to almost nil by the much narrower connecting spaces. These sediments do not yield useful quantities of water and are known as **aquicludes**. When present within or against aquifers they act as barriers to water flow.

The speed at which groundwater moves through an aquifer is governed by the pressure head between two points in saturated sediment, as well as by the resistance to flow. Because of this resistance, the water table mimics the shape of the ground surface (Figure 3.4). If the ground slopes, so too does the water table, with a gradient of difference in height *h*/horizontal distance *l*. It is this gradient that induces flow: the steeper it is, the faster the flow. So, groundwater flow is parallel to that of the ground surface in just the same way as surface water, but it is much slower.

■ What would you expect the natural groundwater flow rate to be beneath the deltaic plains of Bangladesh?

■ The plains have very low surface gradients, so groundwater movement will be sluggish.

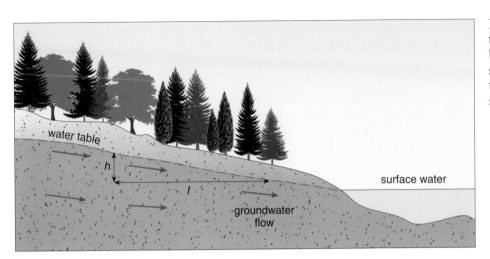

Figure 3.4 The flow of water through a sediment that lies beneath a sloping ground surface. Note how the water table closely follows the ground surface.

This rather obvious conclusion that groundwater movement is slow where the gradient is low is important in the chemical development of groundwater in Bangladesh, and of the sediments that contain it, as you will see later. Since all the rivers and streams have beds made of alluvial sediment, surface water is continually exchanged with groundwater. During high-flow periods, surface water enters the groundwater, while during the dry season escaping groundwater augments river flow (Figure 3.2). Between channels, the water table fluctuates by a few metres as river levels rise and fall seasonally.

The unconsolidated sediments beneath the plains are up to several kilometres thick. This is due to the crust beneath the plains being forced down by the huge load of the Himalaya to the north. Space continually created by this crustal bending is filled by sediments that pour off the rising mountain chain. So the thick sedimentary pile below the plains is partly tectonic in origin, and is one of the world's largest repositories of groundwater. In detail it is far from a simple 'layer cake' that has been laid down stratum by stratum since 50 million years ago, when the India–Eurasia collision began.

3.1.2 Fluctuating sea level and its effects

During the last 2.7 million years, periodic downturns in the global mean surface temperature have resulted in the formation of thick, continental ice sheets at high northern latitudes. Following periods of between 40 000 and 100 000 years, each of these ice sheets melted as global temperatures rose, so the Earth's climate has been involved in a series of cycles.

- ■ What would have been the effects on the oceans of the build-up and then melting of continental ice sheets?

- ▨ The water locked in continental ice sheets ultimately comes from evaporation at the ocean surface. When snow falls on land and is preserved as glacial ice, the volume of ocean water decreases. So, sea level falls during glacial periods. When ice sheets melt, sea level rises.

The last time that continental ice sheets reached their maximum extent, which was about 20 000 years ago, global sea level had fallen by more than 120 m relative to its present level. During the last 18 000 years, warming and melting have caused global sea level to rise by that amount. During the last glacial period, erosion of the Himalaya and the flow of rivers down their slopes would have continued, albeit more slowly because less rain and snow fall during the colder and drier conditions of periods of global cooling. The same processes as those occurring today would have affected the north Indian plain, except for one crucial difference.

■   Suggest what this difference might have been.

▨   The surface of the plains would have been 120 m higher relative to sea level, compared with the few tens of metres above sea level that they are today. The rivers would have cut valleys into an elevated plain that extended further into the Bay of Bengal.

When sea level rose during post-glacial warming, river sediment gradually filled up these valleys as the coastline moved landwards, and created a sequence of young sediment beds in the valleys. Vegetation growing on the surface would have been continually submerged and buried, forming layers rich in organic material between the beds of sediment.

Wells drilled into the deltaic plains reveal how the sediments vary with depth in each well, recording how the glacial to interglacial transitions affected the water-bearing sedimentary layers. Figure 3.5a is a cross-section through the sediments, based on several Bangladeshi well records, as it would appear in a vertical slice cut from west to east. It shows how the base of the unconsolidated sediments is the edge of a broad valley cut into ancient hard rocks, which are exposed in the hills to the east. The orange–brown sediments comprise a sequence of beds with different grain sizes. But these beds are cut by the lower boundary of the darker

Figure 3.5a Schematic cross-section through alluvium beneath the Bangladeshi plains (*Note*: the vertical scale is greatly exaggerated). Colours indicate different ages of unconsolidated sediment, and the various ornaments signify their different grain sizes. The blank area on the right-hand side represents older, hard rocks.

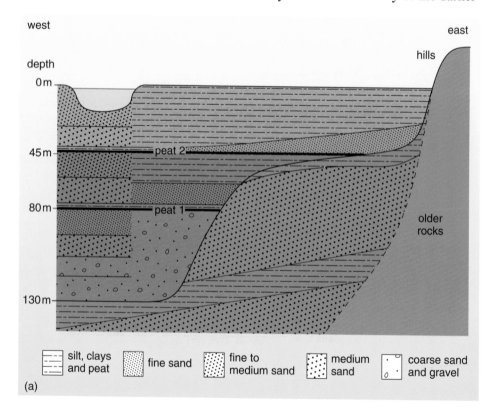

brown sediments, so the orange–brown sediments are *older* than the darker ones. The boundary defines a younger valley that descends around 130 m below sea level at its deepest, as predicted for the last glacial period. The darker brown beds progressively filled the valley, the earliest infill being at the bottom and the youngest at the top. They represent the gradual, post-glacial rise in sea level between 18 000 and 7000 years ago. As well as sands and gravels, the dark-brown sediments contain thin layers of clays and peat (preserved vegetable matter). The peat layers represent dead vegetation that was preserved in swamps. These are similar to the lowland peats that formed during the post-glacial warm period in the Fens of eastern England. British peatlands were never

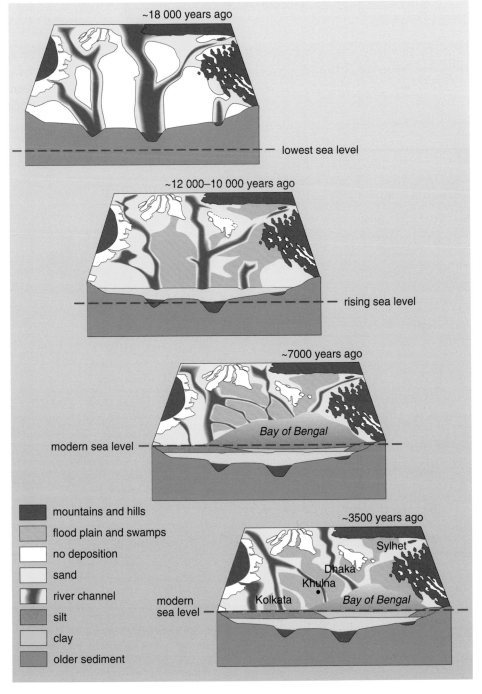

Figure 3.5b Sketch maps of how conditions in the delta changed during sea-level rise between 18 000 and 7000 years ago, and then as sedimentation filled the northern Bay of Bengal from 7000 to 3500 years ago (the sea is now just at bottom right of the map. Note that the lower part of each sketch is a cross-section of how sediments were laid down since 18 000 years ago.

covered with sediment because the crust beneath the British Isles rose as it recovered from being forced down by glacial ice faster than sea level rose. In the case of Bangladesh, buried peat beds are crucially important in explaining the arsenic contamination of groundwater, as you will discover.

Figure 3.5b shows four stages in the evolution of the delta plains as sea level rose, based on cores of sediment recovered from a few tens of deep wells spread across Bangladesh, and analysis of the present landforms. River channels migrated across the flood plain laying down sands, while silts, clays and peats were deposited in flood plains and swamps. These changing conditions laid down the sediments of the delta plains, but the shifting locations of different kinds of sediment make the layering preserved beneath much of today's surface difficult to predict.

Data from wells across Bangladesh reveal the extent of several sediment-filled valleys (Figure 3.6), each of which is likely to contain buried peat and clay layers at depth.

Figure 3.6   (a) Map of the alluvial areas of Bangladesh showing the main river channels at the time of the last glacial maximum. The orange areas are where older alluvium occurs in terraces above general flood levels. (b) Locations of wells (blue squares) from which water has been analysed precisely.

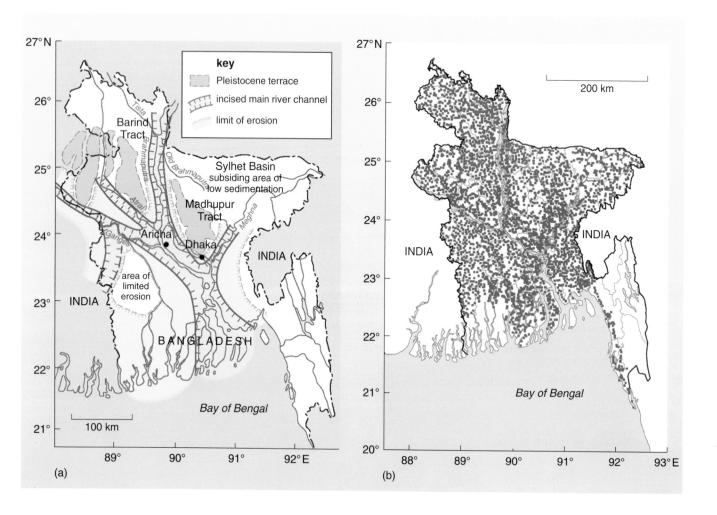

3.2 How minerals react chemically

As well as being broken down, eroded and transported by physical processes, rocks and minerals are chemically changed by processes involved in weathering. Chemical reactions lie at the root of water contamination, and they begin when rocks that formed deep within the Earth eventually reach the surface.

■   Why are many silicate minerals in igneous and metamorphic rocks susceptible to chemical weathering?

▪   They formed under conditions of high pressure and high temperature, so that when they reach the Earth's surface they become unstable.

Quartz (SiO_2) is the one common silicate that does not succumb eventually to chemical weathering. (Note, however, that it can dissolve under some conditions.) It survives to become the dominant mineral in sandy and silty sediments. All other silicates contain alkali (Na, K), alkaline-earth (Ca, Mg) or transition metals (Fe predominantly) that are reactive in the presence of hydrogen ions, i.e. in the slightly acid conditions that are essential for chemical weathering.

Unstable silicates react to different degrees with mildly acidic water. The metals in their structure enter solution as ions, sometimes only temporarily, and the remaining silicate structure becomes hydrated and transformed to that of clay minerals. Some of the silica (SiO_2) also enters solution. Silicate weathering reactions can be expressed in a grossly simplified equation as

$$silicate(s) + H_2O(l) + H^+(aq) = clay(s) + metal\ ions(aq) + SiO_2(aq) \quad (3.1)$$

Hydrogen ions emerge in natural waters from two main processes:

1   solution of carbon dioxide from the air and from respiration of soil bacteria and plant roots;

2   oxidation of sulfide minerals.

You might think that igneous and metamorphic rocks made mainly from silicates would decompose quickly in naturally acid water, especially in a warm, humid climate. In fact, silicate rocks do not weather at all quickly, in human terms. Igneous rocks used to make ancient stone tools found in India (some as old as 700 000 years) show little sign of having been weathered.

■   Why do you think that crystalline igneous and metamorphic rocks are so durable?

▪   In crystalline rocks there are no pore spaces, so water and dissolved ions cannot easily get inside them.

Minerals that originally formed in igneous or metamorphic rocks are 'liberated' from crystalline aggregates by physical weathering and breakage when they are transported. This liberation eventually produces grains small enough to be formed of single minerals. Their molecular structures are then directly in contact with water and any hydrogen ions in it. They can more easily engage in chemical reactions in which they are decomposed. Since the surface of a grain is where chemical reactions can take place, its *surface area* is the controlling factor over its rate of decomposition. The time taken for a grain to decompose completely is given by dividing the mass of the grain by this rate. Volume multiplied by mineral density gives the grain's mass.

Question 3.1

Consider spherical grains of the same reactive mineral with radii of 1 mm (0.001 m or 10^{-3} m) and 0.1 mm (0.0001 m or 10^{-4} m).

(i)   How does the surface area : volume ratio of the smaller grain compare to that of the larger grain?

(ii)   What are the implications in terms of reaction rate?

To work this out, you need to compare the surface areas relative to the volumes of each grain. You can ignore density. Both the surface area and the volume of a spherical grain are related to its radius r:

$$\text{surface area} = 4\pi r^2; \quad \text{volume} = \frac{4\pi}{3}r^3; \quad \pi = 3.14.$$

So a sediment made up of small grains decomposes faster than the same mass of sediment made up of coarser grains. Below the water table, mineral grains are in perpetual contact with water and dissolved ions. This is where much chemical weathering takes place. So, in a sense, 'weathering' is a misnomer, because the grains are not in direct contact with the weather.

Not only do the dominant metals in reactive silicate minerals enter solution during chemical weathering, but so too do elements present in trace amounts. This is one source of dangerous water contamination. Below are the formulae of two silicate minerals that occur commonly in igneous and metamorphic rocks and which are unstable under surface conditions:

amphibole, $(Na,K)Ca_2(Mg,Fe,Al)_5[Si_6Al_2O_{22}](OH,F)_2$

biotite mica, $K_2(Mg,Fe^{2+})_4(Fe^{3+},Al,Ti)_2[Si_6Al_2O_{20}](OH,F)_4$

■   Ignoring the complexity of their formulae, can you foresee a potential health problem should either mineral break down?

▨   Both contain fluoride ions that would be released into water. As you saw in Chapter 2, high levels of fluoride in drinking water cause severe health problems.

The molecular formulae of silicate minerals show only the major elements (O, Si, Al, Ti, Fe, Mg, Ca, K, Na, F and H) that form them. However, naturally occurring minerals are far from pure. Less-common elements substitute for major ones, according to the size of their atoms. A good example is the rare, poisonous metal thallium. In the 1960s, the CIA allegedly considered using thallium to discredit President Fidel Castro of Cuba, by an agent putting it in his socks (thallium is absorbed easily by the skin). One of its early symptoms is loss of hair, and Castro is renowned for his beard. Thallium ingestion of no more than 15 mg kg^{-1} of body mass is lethal. Although not an alkali metal, thallium has the same atomic size as potassium and can therefore substitute for it in feldspar,

(i) small

$SA = 4 \times 3.14 \times (10^{-4} m)^2$
$= 12.56 \times 10^{-8} m$

$V = \frac{4 \times 3.14 \times (10^{-4} m)^3}{3}$
$= 4.19 \times 10^{-12} m$

big

$SA = 4 \times 3.14 \times (10^{-3} m)^2$
$= 12.56 \times 10^{-6} m^2$

$V = \frac{4 \times 3.14 \times (10^{-3})^3}{3}$
$= 4.19 \times 10^{-9} m^2$

$3 \times 10^{-8} : 10^{-12} \quad \frac{3}{10^{-4}}$

$3 \times 10^{-6} : 10^{-9} \quad \frac{3}{10^{-3}}$

R

which weathers easily. Fortunately, the abundance of thallium in ordinary rocks is minuscule and mineral weathering rarely presents a problem.

In the zone of aeration that extends through the sediments above the water table, oxygen is available and diffuses in aqueous solution into the top few metres of groundwater. Oxygen in aqueous solution plays two important roles. On the one hand it supports aerobic bacteria that oxidise and kill many pathogenic bacteria and viruses. Such biogenic oxidation, along with filtration by sediment, helps to purify groundwater; hence its universal attractiveness for domestic water supplies. Because all groundwater has to pass through this aerated zone at some stage in its evolution, even that at much greater depth is generally safe, from a biological standpoint. The second role of dissolved oxygen is its reaction with grains of sulfide minerals freed from rocks when they are physically weathered. The simplest and most common of these is pyrite (FeS_2), which breaks down in the presence of oxygen and water through two linked reactions:

1 Oxidation of sulfur

The sulfur in pyrite is in the form of the S_2^{2-} ion, whose two negative charges balance the two positive charges on Fe^{2+} (iron(II)). All metal sulfides are highly insoluble, but the sulfur in them can be oxidised, with the release of heat in exothermic reactions. Oxygen accepts two electrons from the sulfur in pyrite to form sulfate ions, which are soluble:

$$S_2^{2-} + 4O_2 = 2SO_4^{2-} \tag{3.2}$$

The breakdown reaction of pyrite also involves water, and the full equation is

$$2FeS_2(s) + 7O_2(aq) + 2H_2O(l) = 2Fe^{2+}(aq) + 4H^+(aq) + 4SO_4^{2-}(aq) \tag{3.3}$$

Not only is sulfur oxidised to sulfate ions, but soluble Fe^{2+} ions are freed from the pyrite structure, and breakdown of water releases H^+ ions. Dissolved hydrogen ions create acid conditions, so the product is a dilute mixture of sulfuric acid ($4H^+(aq) + 2SO_4^{2-}(aq)$) and iron(II) sulfate ($2Fe^{2+}(aq) + 2SO_4^{2-}(aq)$).

2 Oxidation of Fe^{2+} ions to Fe^{3+}

If the water still contains oxygen, soluble iron(II) is oxidised to iron(III) in the form of insoluble iron(III) hydroxide, as you saw in Equation 2.5:

$$4Fe^{2+}(aq) + 6H_2O(l) + O_2(aq) = 4FeOOH(s) + 8H^+$$

Remember that FeOOH is the mineral goethite that we are calling iron(III) hydroxide for simplicity (since in nature $Fe(OH)_3$ quickly transforms to goethite, see page 24).

Complete oxidation of pyrite, therefore, produces iron(III) hydroxide and water that contains dilute sulfuric acid. Hydrogen ions released in this way add to chemical weathering of silicates (Equation 3.1). The pyrite oxidation reactions generate heat: they are highly exothermic. Once started, they proceed quickly to completion and rocks rich in pyrite weather easily. Such zones have distinctly yellow–orange–brown outcrops due to the release of iron(III) hydroxide. Even when sediment transportation is fast, as in rivers flowing from the Himalaya, no pyrite survives the journey to be deposited finally in sediments. However, its weathering products do survive. Insoluble iron(III) hydroxide travels in suspension and also forms thin coatings around other transported grains, mainly stable quartz and some mica. Slower weathering of common iron-rich silicates also produces iron(III) hydroxide, which is the most common iron-bearing material in the sedimentary environment.

■ From Equations 3.2 and 3.3, deduce the chemical conditions that encourage the *formation* of sulfides.

■ The sulfide-weathering reactions in Equations 3.2 and 3.3 involve oxidation. When oxygen is available as an electron acceptor the reactions proceed *to the right*. If, on the other hand, electrons are freely available (reducing conditions) the reactions in Equation 3.2 and 3.3 proceed *to the left*, when sulfur in the form of sulphate and the appropriate metal ions are present. So sulfides form under reducing conditions.

Reducing conditions can develop in some sedimentary environments. Stagnant water, in which the finest grains settle slowly from suspension to form silts and clay-rich muds, becomes anaerobic when organic debris in fine sediment decays by bacterial action. First, aerobic bacteria oxidise the organic matter completely to carbon dioxide and water, consuming oxygen in the process. Once all the dissolved oxygen has been used, aerobic bacteria can no longer function in the reducing conditions that result. At this stage anaerobic bacteria take over. However, they cannot completely oxidise vegetable tissue. Consequently, some bacterially degraded organic material remains, eventually to become preserved in the fine sediment. Some groups of anaerobic bacteria generate methane during their metabolism, whereas others get their metabolic energy by reducing sulfate ions to sulfide in hydrogen sulfide gas, thereby accounting for the rotten-eggs smell of swamp gases. In the second case, any iron(II) ions in the water combine with sulfide to precipitate pyrite (FeS_2).

■ Where might the sulfate ions have come from in the rock cycle to help 'fuel' the bacteria that generate hydrogen sulfide?

■ From elsewhere in the cycle through decomposition of sulfides exposed to oxygen (Equations 3.2 and 3.3).

As a result of this reducing biochemistry, most mudstones and shales contain pyrite, which is black when very fine grained. The golden streaks in household coal are coarser pyrite or 'fool's gold'. As you know, seemingly innocuous rocks like these are highly reactive in oxidising conditions because of their pyrite content. You may have seen obnoxious looking yellow–brown–orange slime in the banks of streams, generally where they cut through mudstones or shales. This is iron(III) hydroxide, the ochre once used as a paint pigment. Ochres signify that pyrite in the exposed rock is being oxidised. Their presence is also a good indicator of potential metal pollution and high acidity in stream water. However, as you will learn, iron(III) hydroxide can itself prevent metal pollution from being extreme.

3.3 Where does the arsenic in Bangladesh's groundwater come from?

R

A chemical survey of groundwater in Bangladesh was conducted in the late 1990s by consulting engineers Mott MacDonald International (MMI), the Bangladesh Department of Public Health Engineering (DPHE) and the British Geological Survey (BGS). Its results showed clearly that dangerous levels of arsenic in water from newly sunken deep wells were widespread (see Section 3.4). The most important question, apart from how to remedy the situation (Chapter 5), is 'How did such a rare element as arsenic get into the water?' Ultimately, in the absence of any significant industrial sources in Bangladesh, it must have come from the Himalaya, either in the river water that recharges the groundwater or in mineral grains carried by rivers from the Himalaya and deposited as sediments on the plains. Tracking down the causes by scientific investigation is essential in assessing where similar problems might occur in other parts of the world. Since groundwater presents the best source of domestic water for the whole Bangladeshi population, specific causes of arsenic contamination, and where they take place, need to be identified. It may be possible to avoid sources of natural arsenic pollution by using data from such research.

The chemical properties of arsenic are quite complicated. It is a rare element and enters common silicate minerals in only minute traces. Most arsenic resides in sulfide minerals, especially pyrite, which occurs at levels of between 0.1% and 1.0% in many sedimentary, igneous and metamorphic rocks that form the Himalaya.

Question 3.2

Do you think that grains of pyrite carried from the Himalaya into Bangladesh by the main rivers and deposited there can account for the arsenic pollution? Give a reason for your answer.

Any arsenic once contained in Himalayan sulfides ends up in river water or shallow groundwater, probably very soon after the pyrite is exposed to chemical weathering. All natural water contains some dissolved arsenic, as well as almost all other elements, but usually at concentrations that are far too low to cause health problems. Indeed, until the development of modern water-analysis methods most dissolved elements could not be detected, let alone measured in surface water and groundwater. In fact, there is an important reason why arsenic in particular generally poses no problem in most domestic water supplies from beneath the surface. It results from one of the very products of pyrite oxidation itself – iron(III) hydroxide.

■ In what manner is iron(III) hydroxide, produced by pyrite oxidation and weathering of iron-bearing silicates, carried in rivers? Under what conditions will it be deposited?

■ Like all chemical precipitates, iron(III) hydroxide is very fine grained, so it travels in suspension. A very low-energy environment is required for it to settle out. Settling can be so slow that even in stagnant water it may take a long time.

Sands and gravels in the beds of rivers are usually made of clean mineral and rock fragments, because few suspended materials are deposited at the water speeds at which large grains just cease to move. In slack water, larger grains do become coated with suspended material, such as mud and silt, sometimes bound to them by bacterial or algal films. Iron(III) hydroxide is so fine that it also seeps with river water into underlying sediments, and eventually coats all the grains in them. Even in minute veneers it is the principal colorant of sediments, imparting characteristic yellows, oranges and browns. What is the significance of this?

Figure 3.7   The molecular structure of goethite, FeOOH, which we are referring to as iron(III) hydroxide (blue = iron; red = oxygen; white = hydrogen). This is a complex structure and you need not understand the complexities of the bonding, but simply note the relative openness of the structure.

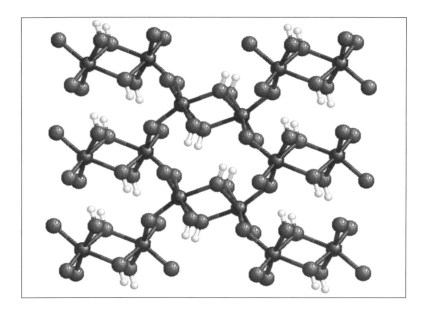

R   Iron(III) hydroxide has a remarkable capacity to capture ions of other elements. This is because of its molecular structure (Figure 3.7), which is full of gaps. Effectively, hydrogen atoms are remote enough from iron and oxygen in the structure for them to produce localised positive charges at the surface of mineral particles. Consequently, negatively charged anions can attach to the *surface* of iron(III) hydroxide; this process is known as **adsorption**, as opposed to *ab*sorption in which ions enter the *body* of a molecular structure. It is not just simple ions of non-metals that carry negative charges. There are negatively charged **complex ions** in which non-metals or metals combine with oxygen. Examples are PO_4^{3-}, AsO_4^{3-}, SeO_4^{2-}, SO_4^{2-}, NO_3^- and oxygen-bearing complex ions of several metals, such as Cr, Mo, V and W (e.g. CrO_4^{2-}). Iron(III) hydroxide, therefore, acts like a chemical 'mop'. Complex arsenic-bearing ions such as AsO_4^{3-} (arsenate) are 'mopped' up. There is a limit to how much arsenic can be adsorbed in this way, and ions such as arsenate 'compete' for available sites with other negatively charged ions in the water. An equilibrium between all such ions in solution and those adsorbed is reached while water chemistry remains constant. However, if concentrations in solution of some competing ions increase for some reason while that of arsenate ions does not, competing ions may displace adsorbed arsenate back into solution (Section 3.3.2).

[handwritten margin note:] Small particles of Iron(III) have greater surface area so adsorb more arsenate. However, imbalance ...

■   Bearing in mind the answer to Question 3.1, what size of iron(III) hydroxide particles are most efficient in adsorbing arsenic?

▨   The smaller the particles are, the greater their surface area relative to their volume and, therefore, the more effective they are at adsorbing arsenic.

R   Particles formed by precipitation are extremely small, a few nanometres (10^{-9} m) across. A minutely thin iron(III) hydroxide coating on sedimentary grains acts effectively as a natural pollution preventive. However, by adsorbing toxic elements such as arsenic the coating becomes a potential threat itself. If chemical conditions change, then the veneer might decompose, thereby releasing the adsorbed elements.

The systematic chemical survey of well waters by MMI, DPHE and BGS covers Bangladesh almost uniformly (Figure 3.6b) and includes the depth of each well. Wells range from less than 10 m to more than 350 m deep, and water from 3552 of them was analysed. Plotting arsenic concentration against well depth should reveal if there is a relationship between contamination and different depths in the alluvial aquifers (Figure 3.8).

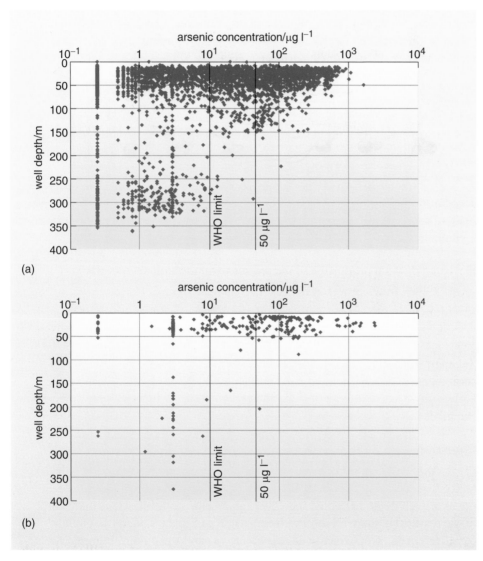

(a)

(b)

Figure 3.8   Plots of arsenic concentration against well depth: (a) in all wells involved in the survey; (b) in 270 wells from three districts of Bangladesh with known incidences of arsenic-related ailments. *Note*: the arsenic scale is logarithmic. It shows the orders of magnitude of arsenic concentration relative to the WHO maximum recommended concentration of $10 \ \mu g \ l^{-1}$ and the Bangladesh limit of $50 \ \mu g \ l^{-1}$. Such plots spread the data so that individual points are more easily seen. Another feature of these plots is that, at very low concentrations ($<1 \ \mu g \ l^{-1}$), vertical distributions of a single value show up. This is because the results of 0.2, 0.3, etc. are close to the precision of $\pm 0.1 \ \mu g \ l^{-1}$.

Note that in Figure 3.8 the density of dots that represent arsenic concentrations decreases with depth. This is because there are fewer deep wells than shallow ones: it is cheaper to sink wells down to 100 m than to greater depths, and also shallow wells can be driven using simple technology (Figure 1.1c).

Question 3.3

From Figure 3.8: (a) do all the wells from the whole survey (Figure 3.8a) contain arsenic concentrations above the WHO recommended maximum? (b) If not, which wells are the most and which the least risky? (c) Does the pattern shown by data for the special study areas (Figure 3.8b) match that for the whole country?

The answer to Question 3.3 suggests that shallow groundwater poses the greatest risk from arsenic, and that wells deeper than 150 m tend to be much less affected. The next step is to look for a correlation with physical changes in the alluvial sediments with depth. Figure 3.9 shows the variation with depth of grain size and colour of sediments in a typical well affected by arsenic contamination. Plots of this kind show grain size increasing away from the depth axis, to reflect the classification of sediments into clays, silts, fine-, medium- and coarse-grained sands, and gravels, each of which is assigned a different ornament on the figure. The colours approximate those of sediments recovered from the well during drilling.

■   Try to explain these colour variations in terms of the most likely mineral that causes coloration.

▨   The principal colorant in sediments is iron(III) hydroxide. The orange sediments contain more of that mineral than the grey ones, which contain little, if any iron(III) hydroxide.

The coloration of the grey sediments is mainly due to fine-grained organic matter (incompletely decayed vegetation). The presence of peat layers is common in many shallow wells.

■   Roughly what proportion of the sediments in the well should give abundant groundwater supplies?

▨   More than 90% of the sediments in the well are sandy aquifers. Silt and clay aquicludes do occur, but they are very thin.

So, apart from being contaminated with arsenic, the well shown in Figure 3.9 should give excellent yields. Yet it gives the first indication of the connection between arsenic contamination and the geology underlying much of Bangladesh.

Question 3.4

(a)   Compare the information shown in Figure 3.9 with the plot of arsenic concentration against depth for all wells analysed (Figure 3.8a). Does the range of well depths affected most by high arsenic concentrations match any of the features in the well information? (b) From Figure 3.5a, try to explain any discrepancies between your answers to (a) and the data in Figure 3.8a. Suggest which sediments beneath Bangladesh are the regional source of arsenic contamination.

Question 3.5

The grey sediments in Figure 3.9 do contain iron, but in the form of small amounts of fine-grained pyrite, as well as a lot of organic matter. Are conditions in them oxidising (aerobic) or reducing (anaerobic)?

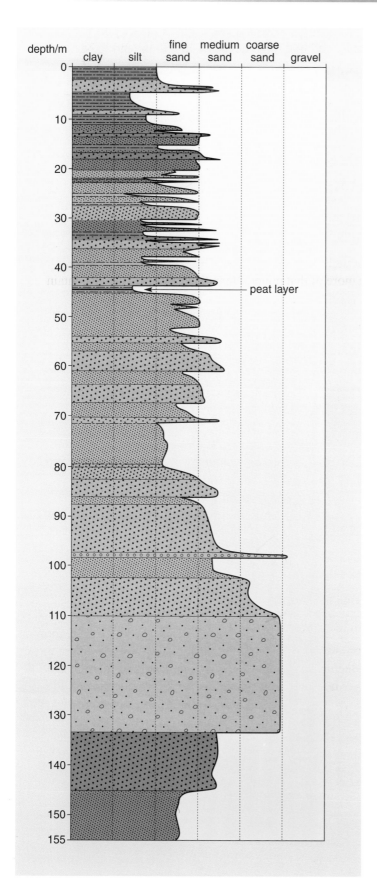

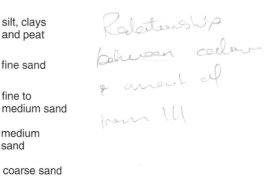

peat layer

Figure 3.9 Variation of the grain size and the colour of sediment encountered down an arsenic-contaminated well in Bangladesh. Orange sediments occur continuously below 155 m in deeper wells. The grain size variations found within the sediments are signified by the 'zigzag' right-hand edge of the section – the further to the right that the line extends, the coarser are the grains in the sediment (the scale is not quantitative, but divided into categories based on visual inspection of the sediments).

The answers to Questions 3.3 to 3.5 implicate four connections with arsenic contamination:

- the shallowest and, therefore, youngest sediments beneath the plains
- grey sediments
- the presence within the sediments of peat layers (made almost entirely of partly decayed vegetation)
- reducing, anaerobic conditions.

Interestingly, some of the contaminated wells emit methane. The methane is generated by anaerobic bacteria (Section 3.2) that metabolise peat and fragments of dead vegetation in the grey sands. So that is a fifth connection. You are now in a position to look at hypotheses that focus on how the arsenic is released to groundwater.

Three mechanisms have been invoked to explain arsenic contamination of the groundwater:

1   Arsenic is released by oxidation of pyrite grains in the alluvial sediments that show evidence for reducing conditions, if atmospheric oxygen gets into the aquifer (pyrite oxidation, Section 3.3.1).

2   Arsenic-bearing anions (e.g. AsO_4^{3-}) adsorbed by iron(III) hydroxide are displaced into solution by exchange of phosphate (PO_4^{3-}) anions derived from overapplication of fertiliser to surface soils (phosphate competition, Section 3.3.2).

3   Anaerobic conditions permit the dissolution of iron(III) hydroxide and reduction of iron(III) to soluble iron(II). This dissolves the hydroxide grain coatings and releases their adsorbed arsenic to solution (reductive dissolution, Section 3.3.3). (*Note*: if sulfate ions are available, then Equations 3.2 and 3.3, aided by sulfate–sulfide bacteria, can also reverse to form iron sulfide, thereby explaining the pyrite content of the reduced sedimentary layers.)

You will now examine each mechanism in more detail, using some geochemical evidence.

3.3.1 Pyrite oxidation

Because the levels in the sediments that yield arsenic-contaminated water show clear indications of reducing conditions, apart from in the top 35 m of Figure 3.9 where they are interlayered with oxidised sediments, pyrite oxidation would seem to be the least likely option. Nonetheless, it was widely believed to be the culprit because sulfide oxidation is a well-documented source of arsenic pollution in mining areas. Oxygen might enter the sediments by groundwater flow, or if the water table fell due to pumping, to start pyrite oxidation. However, oxidation cannot be complete if pyrite remains.

■   What are the three main products of iron sulfide oxidation?

■   Sulfate ions (SO_4^{2-}), hydrogen ions and iron(III) hydroxide.

So groundwater in which pyrite is being oxidised should become more acid and rich in sulfate.

Question 3.6

Figure 3.10 shows plots of arsenic concentrations against (a) those of sulfate ions, and (b) pH. Briefly explain how these data either confirm or refute the hypothesis that oxidation of pyrite could contribute to arsenic contamination.

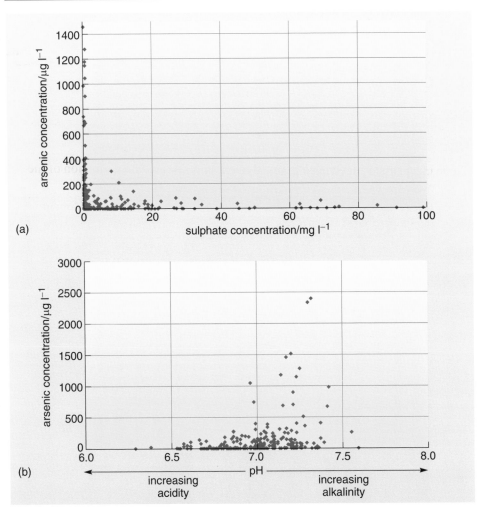

Figure 3.10 Plots of arsenic concentration in groundwater from the special study area against those for: (a) sulfate ions; (b) pH. *Note*: pH is a measure of dissolved hydrogen ion abundance and, therefore, acidity. A value of 7 indicates neutral conditions; values <7 indicate acid conditions; value >7 indicate alkalinity.

You will have noticed that many very shallow wells (<30 m deep) in the special study area are also arsenic contaminated (Figure 3.8b), but they penetrate some orange (oxidised) sediments (Figure 3.9).

■ Does this imply that arsenic in very shallow wells is being released by oxidation of pyrite?

▪ No, because the arsenic in them is unrelated to either pH or sulfate concentrations.

3.3.2 Phosphate competition for arsenic in iron(III) hydroxide

Iron(III) hydroxide adsorbs a great range of complex anions, including phosphate (PO_4^{3-}). Phosphorus and arsenic are in the same group in the Periodic Table (Figure 2.3) and large amounts of water-soluble phosphates in fertiliser have been added to fields since the beginning of the 20th century. This possible mechanism would therefore indicate a human influence over the arsenic contamination, if confirmed. Figure 3.11a plots arsenic concentration against phosphate concentration in all well waters analysed. Take a few minutes to examine Figure 3.11 and decide what each plot shows. This will help you to answer the questions that follow.

Figure 3.11 Plots of (a) arsenic concentration in groundwater against that for phosphate ions (PO_4^{3-}), and (b) well depth versus phosphate concentrations from all wells analysed in Bangladesh.

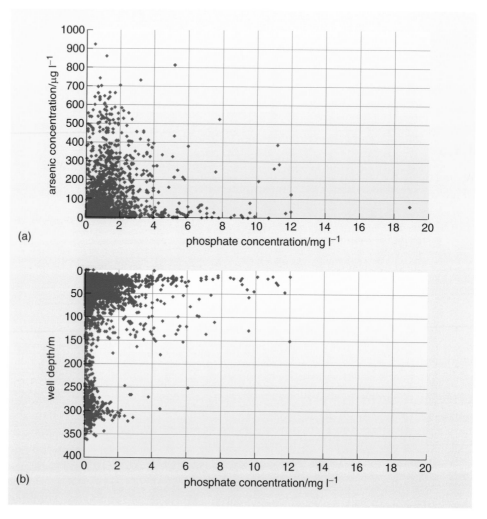

■ If the hypothesis were true, how would you expect phosphate concentrations and arsenic concentrations to appear in Figure 3.11a?

▪ High arsenic concentrations should be associated with high phosphate concentrations.

In fact, phosphate concentrations reach higher values in Bangladesh groundwater than in that from most other parts of the world, yet most high arsenic concentrations (100 to 1000 μg l^{-1}) are associated with the lower range of phosphate concentrations (0 to 4 mg l^{-1}). This does not refute the hypothesis that phosphate in fertiliser is implicated, because a few water samples on Figure 3.11a do show high arsenic concentrations associated with high phosphorus concentrations. However, another observation casts further doubt on it.

If phosphate is entering groundwater from fertilisers, then you would expect its concentration to decrease as depth increases. But the distribution of phosphate in groundwater is not as simple as that. Look at Figure 3.11b and then tackle Question 3.7.

Question 3.7

(a) Describe the way in which phosphate concentration varies with well depth. (b) Suggest an explanation for any pattern that you can see. (c) How do your observations compare with the hypothesis that phosphate from fertilisers is replacing arsenic from iron(III) hydroxide?

Again, geochemical data sideline this hypothesis except, possibly, for the shallowest wells.

3.3.3 Reductive dissolution of iron(III) hydroxide

Testing the hypothesis of reductive dissolution of iron(III) hydroxide hinges on which other elements are likely to be released to solution by the same process.

■ Suggest ions, other than iron(II), which would be released to solution when iron(III) hydroxide is dissolved under reducing conditions.

■ In Section 3.3 you learned that complex ions such as PO_4^{3-}, SeO_4^{2-}, SO_4^{2-}, NO_3^- and those of several metals, such as Cr, Mo, V and W, as well as AsO_4^{3-}, are adsorbed by iron(III) hydroxide.

So there are many possible geochemical plots that might refute or help to confirm this hypothesis. You have already looked at the arsenic–phosphate relationship (Figure 3.11a), and that gives some support. It might explain some of the high phosphorus concentrations in the grey sediment zone down to 130 m. Sulfate ions (Figure 3.10a) may be reduced to sulfide by bacterial action in anaerobic waters, and are therefore unreliable indicators. Of the others, only dissolved iron(II) and molybdenum ions were analysed in the MMI/DPHE/BGS survey. They are plotted against arsenic in Figure 3.12.

Question 3.8

Examine Figures 3.12a and 3.12b. Do variations of iron(II) and molybdenum concentrations with arsenic concentrations provide any support for the reductive dissolution of iron(III) hydroxide?

The results conflict; however, there is a plausible explanation for the lack of correlation of iron(II) with arsenic. If sulfide ions were being generated from sulfate ions by anaerobic bacteria living in reducing, arsenic-contaminated groundwater, then iron(II) would be precipitated as sulfide (pyrite). This would consume sulfate ions as well, thereby neatly accounting for low sulfate levels in arsenic-rich water (Figure 3.10a). Microscopic examination of samples of the grey, reduced sediments shows irregular grains of pyrite, probably formed by precipitation after deposition of the sediments.

■ How does the formation of sulfides in the reduced sediments complicate the arsenic picture?

Figure 3.12 Plots of arsenic concentration in groundwater against that for (a) dissolved iron(II) (Fe^{2+} ions) in all analysed wells, and (b) dissolved molybdenum from wells in the special study areas.

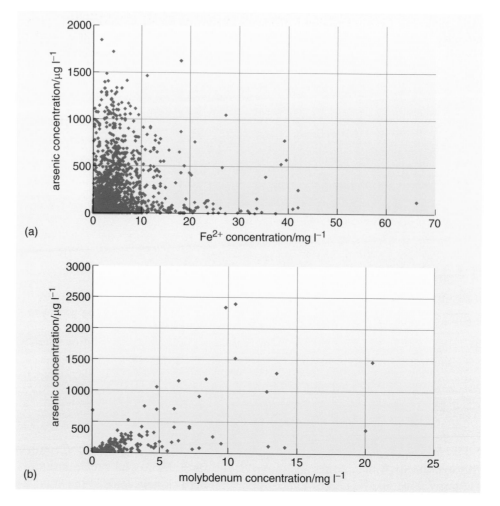

- Arsenic can enter pyrite, thereby drawing down contamination that results from iron(III) hydroxide dissolution. As you will see in Section 3.4, this process has some interesting implications for assessing the risk of arsenic contamination.

Of the three hypotheses, that for reductive dissolution of iron(III) hydroxide gets most support from the geochemical evidence. However, the process of reduction that is most likely to contribute to arsenic contamination is complex, even when considered from a purely inorganic standpoint. The release of methane from contaminated wells points also to a biological factor: the consumption of organic matter by anaerobic, methanogenic bacteria.

The contaminated water in Bangladesh comes from a depth in the sediments that contains peats as well as organic matter scattered through the other sediments, which anaerobic bacteria cannot oxidise completely. Carbon-bearing products of this bacterial breakdown of peat are methane and weak organic acids, such as ethanoic acid (CH_3COOH, Box 2.1). So conditions in the peat-rich layers of the sediments are both highly reducing and weakly acidic. Ethanoic acid dissociates in water to yield ethanoate (CH_3COO^-) and hydrogen ions. In the presence of dissolved carbon dioxide (as carbonic acid, H_2CO_3), ethanoate ions reduce and decompose iron(III) hydroxide:

$$8FeOOH(s) + CH_3COO^-(aq) + 15H_2CO_3(aq) \rightarrow 8Fe^{2+}(aq) + 17HCO_3^-(aq) + 12H_2O \qquad (3.4)$$

The hypothesis of bacterial control of reductive dissolution of iron(III) hydroxide in arsenic contamination of Bangladeshi groundwater is largely the result of work by members of the London Arsenic Group at University College, London in association with Mr Peter Ravenscroft, formerly of MMI.

Reductive dissolution of iron(III) hydroxide is now widely regarded as the source of arsenic contamination in Bangladeshi groundwater. Knowing roughly the processes, and the conditions that encourage them, is a major step in both seeking means of remediating the problem and understanding where risks from waterborne arsenic are most likely to occur. Before proceeding to risk, have a look at Figure 3.13, produced by the London Arsenic Group, which summarises the most likely coincidence of circumstances that lie behind the Bangladesh arsenic tragedy.

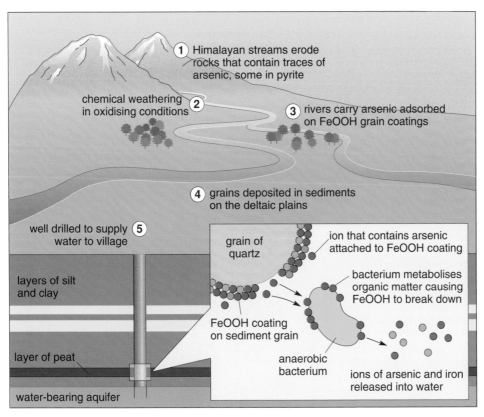

Figure 3.13 Simplified summary of how arsenic most probably enters groundwater in Bangladesh. The inset shows the involvement of anaerobic bacteria in arsenic release from iron(III) hydroxide grain coatings (red is arsenic, grey is iron, blue is oxygen and green is hydrogen ions). Note that oxygen is shown migrating to the bacterium. Iron(III) acts as an electron acceptor and is thus a means of helping the bacterium partially oxidise organic matter, while being reduced itself.

3.4 Assessing the risks

In Chapter 2 you saw that arsenic poses a health hazard and how the physiological consequence of exposure can be assessed by considering the risk of developing various ailments from increasing concentrations of arsenic in drinking water. To all intents, the element itself and ions containing it (e.g. AsO_4^{3-}) are poisons in the proper sense. Except for the possibility that very low levels of arsenic are necessary for mammalian growth (Section 2.2.1), the low concentration side of its dose–response curve (Figure 2.2) is of little concern. The risk of contracting arsenicosis and various cancers increases linearly as its concentration increases (Section 2.3).

There are two other aspects to risk from exposure to arsenic. The first concerns the *geographic likelihood of exposure*. The survey of well-water chemistry in

Bangladesh reveals the chances of arsenic concentration being above levels deemed safe, together with the magnitude of contamination according to where one lives (Section 3.4.1). As you will see, this local risk is not as simple as it might seem, for geological reasons. The second aspect is also geographic, but on a global scale. The tragedy that arose in Bangladesh and neighbouring West Bengal in India came as a malignant surprise to the public and geoscientists alike. Research eventually revealed that it was entirely due to geological conditions. Perhaps there are other parts of the world where the same circumstances conspire to present a risk that has yet to be discovered (Section 3.4.2).

3.4.1 The geography of arsenic contamination in Bangladesh

R

Of the estimated 6 million wells in Bangladesh, water samples from only 3500 (about 0.05%) were analysed in the geochemical survey. The most important matter to address in analysing the risk of exposure is whether or not a particular village lies in an area where arsenic concentrations are above safe levels. Concentrations can be represented on a map by colour coding the arsenic concentration in *individual* wells analysed (Figure 3.14a). Figure 3.14b shows the depth of each well in a similar way. It is also possible to estimate the *continuous* distribution of arsenic concentrations in well water as zones, by predicting arsenic concentrations *between* individual wells (Figure 3.15a).

Figure 3.14 Colour-coded maps of all analysed wells in Bangladesh that show:
(a) arsenic concentrations;
(b) well depth. Note that the colours refer to *ranges* of values.

The four maps shown in Figures 3.14 and 3.15 enable you to *visualise* relationships between arsenic contamination of well water and a variety of

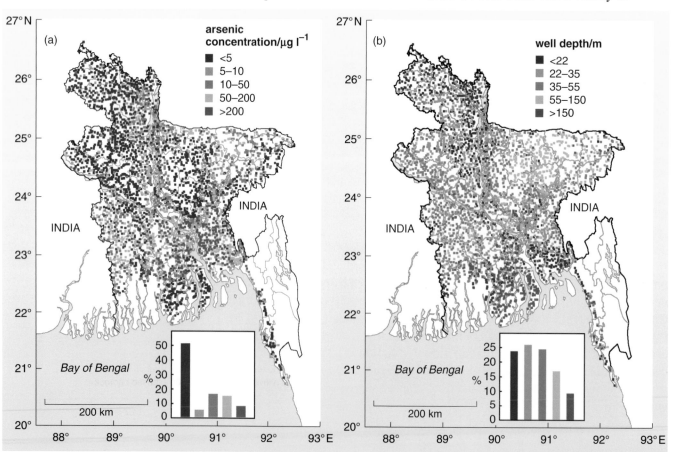

geographic factors. For the maps showing arsenic concentrations, note that wells with levels below 50 μg l^{-1} are assigned blue and green colours, whereas those more highly affected are shown in red and orange. This choice of 'cold' and 'warm' colours is an easily understood way of communicating graphically 'safe' and 'hazardous' areas. We can now compare the answer to Question 3.3 – that hazardous arsenic contamination is associated with wells that are shallower than 150 m while deeper wells are generally safe – with Figures 3.14 and 3.15.

You can see by comparing Figures 3.14b and 3.15a that arsenic occurs at dangerous concentrations mainly in an E–W belt between 22.5° N and 23.5° N, where the affected wells are generally less than 150 m deep. This confirms the answer to Question 3.3. In the area to the northwest of 91° E and 24° N, most of the wells are less than 55 m deep, but the arsenic concentrations do not confirm the answer to Question 3.3. Apart from some wells along the course of the Brahmaputra that exceed 50 μg l^{-1}, most contain arsenic below the level adopted as the maximum permitted (those showing as dark and light blue, and green). All the wells deeper than 150 m, wherever they are situated, seem to provide groundwater with low arsenic concentrations. Most of these safe deep wells are in the lowest part of the delta plain.

The next thing to judge is whether or not the known surface and subsurface geology can be used as a guide as to where arsenic might be expected to be above or below dangerous levels.

Figure 3.15 (a) Contoured map of arsenic concentrations in Bangladeshi well waters, interpolated from Figure 3.14a. Note the broad zone of high arsenic concentrations that runs east–west across the lower part of the delta plain.
(b) Simplified geological map of Bangladesh. Alluvial fan deposits are laid down where small, high-energy streams from the hills reach the plains and deposit their load of sediment in low-angled cones. Bold lines enclose districts in Bangladesh with known incidences of arsenicosis. Study areas are outlined in bold black.

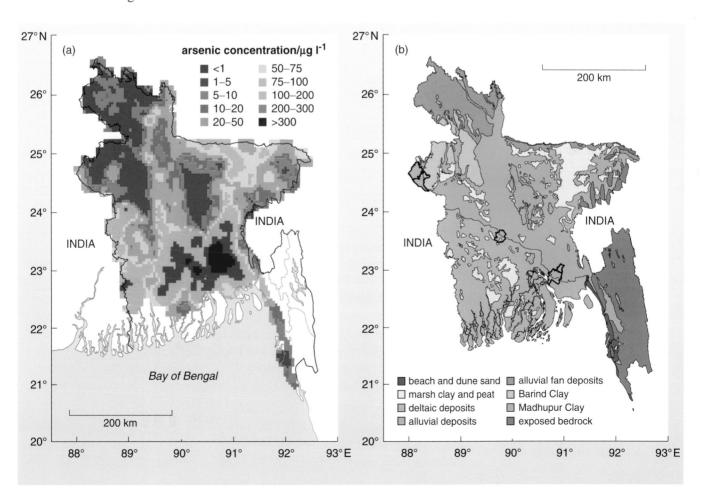

Question 3.9

Compare Figures 3.15a and b, and Figure 3.6a. (a) Are any of the exposed geological units shown on Figure 3.15b consistently associated with high arsenic concentrations in groundwater or are any usually unaffected? In other words, is there any clear relationship between surface geology and arsenic? Look at Figure 3.6a and suggest reasons for your observations. (b) Is there a clearer relationship between the arsenic concentration map (Figure 3.15a) and features on Figure 3.6a?

Surface geology is not a particularly good indicator of where high arsenic concentration might be present, but the map showing subsurface features (Figure 3.6a) reveals clear correlations with the worst affected areas.

The colour-coded map for arsenic concentration in well waters (Figure 3.15a) is useful for visualising risk at the regional scale, but it has some inherent problems.

■ Look at the histogram on Figure 3.14a. (a) What is the percentage of the wells analysed that have arsenic concentrations above 50 μg l^{-1}, the maximum specified by the Government of Bangladesh, and (b) above 10 μg l^{-1}, the WHO maximum?

▨ (a) About 25% are above 50 μg l^{-1}; (b) about 44% are above 10 μg l^{-1}.

Clearly, there are large tracts of the country that pose low risks from drinking groundwater supplied by existing wells. On Figure 3.15b, three special study areas where risk from arsenic contamination ranges from moderate (20 to 75 μg l^{-1}) to very high (>300 μg l^{-1}) are outlined by bold black lines. The arsenic concentration–well depth relationship in these 'at risk' areas is shown by Figure 3.8b. Notice that the majority of wells are less than 50 m deep.

■ Approximately what proportion of the wells less than 50 m deep in the special study areas (Figure 3.8b) have arsenic concentration above 50 μg l^{-1}?

▨ About half are contaminated by arsenic concentrations above the limit set by the Bangladeshi authorities.

R

So, compared with the countrywide situation, people in the special study areas are about five times more likely to be exposed to a hazard from arsenic in drinking water. However, visual evaluation of data does not take into account the way that wells are distributed geographically. Statistical analysis of the way arsenic concentrations in well water varies geographically quantifies the probability of people being exposed to hazardous drinking water according to where they live (Figure 3.16). The calculations are performed in terms of the *magnitude* of the hazard, as expressed by concentrations above different limits. Figure 3.16 shows the ranges of probabilities for the maximum limit set by the WHO (10 μg l^{-1}), that set by the Bangladeshi authorities (50 μg l^{-1}), and two that pose much greater hazards (200 and 400 μg l^{-1}).

R D

The two maps showing probabilities for exposure to arsenic at concentrations >10 μg l^{-1} and >50 μg l^{-1} outline areas for concern that cover about one-half and one-third of Bangladesh respectively. The two maps based on much higher concentrations highlight the areas likely to be most prone to severe arsenic-

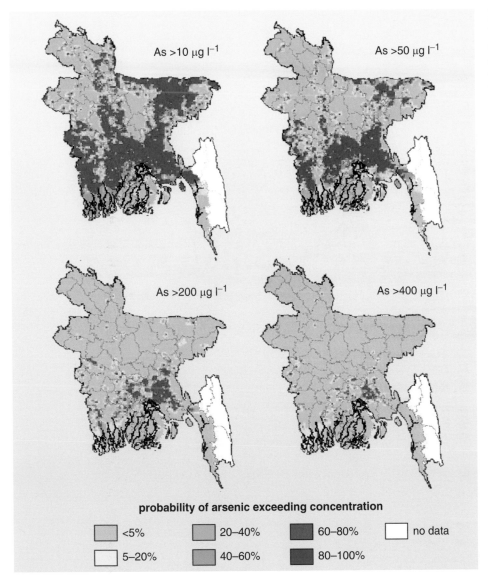

related health problems, both now and in the future. These are areas that decision makers might decide have the highest priorities for remedial measures (Chapter 4).

Statistical evaluations are useful for broad decision making at the scale of administrative districts, but the real effects of arsenic concern individual wells that supply water to families. Arsenic concentrations in individual wells have a specific geochemical cause that is related to the local underlying sediments (Section 3.3) and can confound statisticians. Local aspects of risk emerge from comparing arsenic concentrations in wells that are close to one another. In some villages, one well can have dangerously high concentrations, whereas another close by provides safe water. Figure 3.17 provides one explanation based on the influence of anaerobic bacteria that break down dead vegetable tissue in peat layers to produce methane (Section 3.3.3).

One detail about well design, which you may not have come across before, appears in Figure 3.17. For most of its length, a drilled well or tubewell, as opposed to one dug by hand to a shallow depth, is sealed from the sediments and

R

Figure 3.17 Local variability in arsenic concentrations in well water: (a) wells in the village of Mandari; (b) diagram showing adjacent wells affected differently by arsenic contamination, in relation to well depth and the presence of peat layers in alluvial sediments.

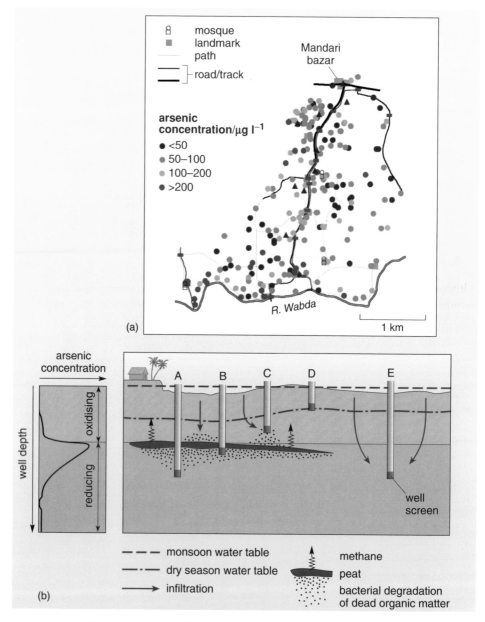

groundwater that it penetrates by a metal tube. Water enters the well only through a perforated section (its 'screen') at the very bottom of the tube, so that pumping is from this level and slightly deeper. Water from higher levels that may be contaminated is excluded.

Question 3.10

From what you learned in Section 3.3.3, which of the wells (A–E) in Figure 3.17 are likely to be contaminated with arsenic, and which are probably safe? Give your reasons.

There is another plausible explanation for unpredictable arsenic concentrations in well waters that is connected with biological activity, which Section 3.2 and the first part of Section 3.3.3 should help you to suggest.

■   What might that explanation be?

■   Another group of anaerobic bacteria thrives in the presence of sulfate ions (SO_4^{2-}), which they reduce to generate hydrogen sulfide. Iron(II) ions released to solution by dissolution of iron(III) hydroxide combine with sulfide ions to form pyrite. Since that mineral can include arsenic, such a process may be *removing* arsenic that might otherwise be in solution.

Although complicating the interpretation of well water analyses, both these factors potentially offer means of remediation of the problem in affected areas (Chapter 4).

Arsenic clearly presents a health risk to a large proportion of Bangladeshis who live in parts of the country underlain by peat-bearing alluvium. The emergence of this risk and a plausible, albeit quite complex reason for it might suggest that similar problems may exist elsewhere in the world.

3.4.2 The rest of the world

Although waterborne arsenic is a problem in metal mining areas, these are geographically small and the risk is easily predictable. The Ganges–Brahmaputra plain is very much larger, and similar low-lying plains are widespread. If arsenic contaminated the groundwater beneath other major river basins, it would constitute one of the world's largest single health threats. Figure 3.18 shows three categories of groundwater supplies. Outlines of major river basins are

Figure 3.18 World distribution of groundwater resources. *Note:* there is a larger version of this image on the DVD-ROM.

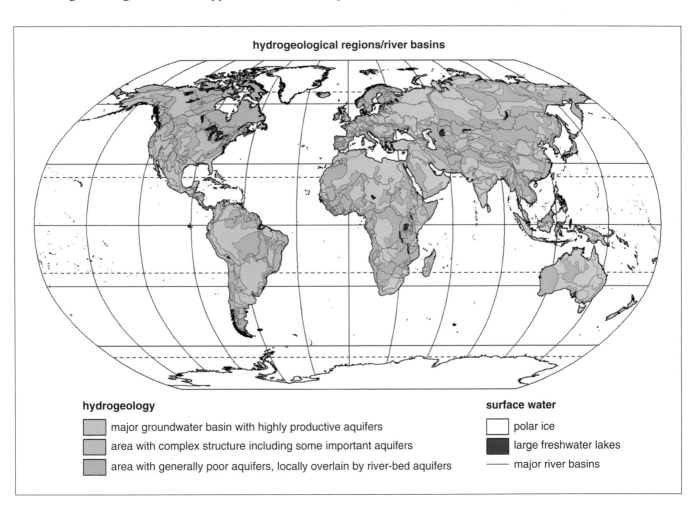

hydrogeological regions/river basins

hydrogeology

☐ major groundwater basin with highly productive aquifers

☐ area with complex structure including some important aquifers

☐ area with generally poor aquifers, locally overlain by river-bed aquifers

surface water

☐ polar ice

■ large freshwater lakes

— major river basins

shown in purple, and all the areas underlain by thick unconsolidated sediments – major, structurally simple groundwater basins with highly productive aquifers – are included in the blue category. How is it possible to predict which of these basins might present arsenic problems similar to those in the Ganges–Brahmaputra plains?

Question 3.11

(a) Write down the three main factors that have contributed to arsenic contamination in the groundwater of Bangladesh. (b) For each factor, suggest topographic and climatic features that might lead to arsenic contamination in any of the blue areas on Figure 3.18.

Figure 3.19 shows maps of world climatic zones and topographic elevation. Together with Figure 3.18, they should enable you to make an approximate assessment of where there may be significant risk from arsenic in groundwater.

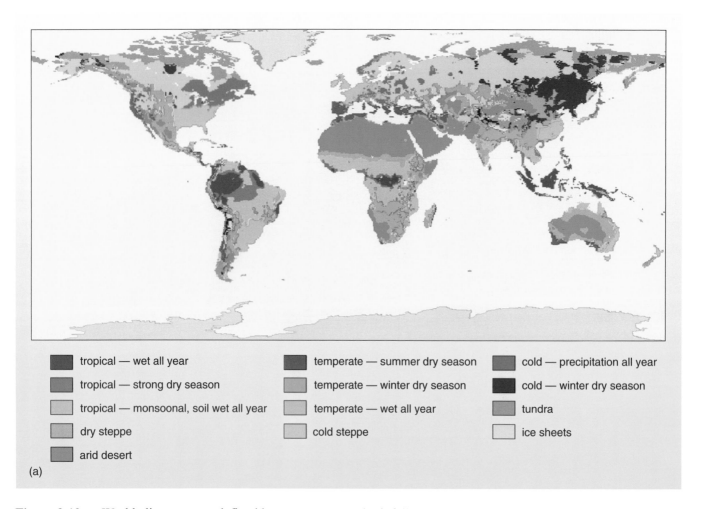

■ tropical — wet all year	■ temperate — summer dry season	■ cold — precipitation all year
■ tropical — strong dry season	■ temperate — winter dry season	■ cold — winter dry season
■ tropical — monsoonal, soil wet all year	■ temperate — wet all year	■ tundra
■ dry steppe	■ cold steppe	■ ice sheets
■ arid desert		

(a)

Figure 3.19a   World climate zones defined by temperature and rainfall. *Note*: there is a larger version of this image on the DVD-ROM.

(b)

Figure 3.19b   Map of surface elevation. The blues are land close to sea level, the darkest being only a few metres above it. Colours then range through a sequence of dark to pale greens, then yellows to greys and white, which is the highest land surface. *Note:* there is a larger version of this image on the DVD-ROM.

Activity 3.1

Allow 30 minutes

By considering the broad factors implicated in arsenic contamination of Bangladeshi well waters (see Answer to Question 3.11), suggest areas elsewhere in the world that satisfy similar conditions. Such areas could be prone to the same problem.

You will need to compare the three maps in Figures 3.18 and 3.19 (larger versions are on the S250 DVD-ROM) to identify areas where the factors coincide. You may be unfamiliar with using maps in this way, but you should be able to make a broad assessment if you keep your study simple. *This is not intended to be an exhaustive search.* Your knowledge from this chapter and the scale of the maps restrict you to large basins underlain by unconsolidated sediments. Areas that have dry climates will have problems from *lack* of groundwater, and will be sparsely populated. Areas with cold to frigid climates can also be ignored. The crucial factor in Bangladesh was that vegetation had been buried by sediment, so humid areas in which plants grow both densely and quickly are important. The topographic factor should be obvious from Figure 3.19b. The colours you should be looking for on Figures 3.18 and 3.19 are in Table 3.1. Figure 3.20 is a blank political map of the world on which you can mark coincidences. An atlas will help identify country names.

Figure 3.20 Blank political map of the world.

Table 3.1   Colours on Figures 3.18 and 3.19 that give clues to areas of the world where groundwater may be arsenic rich because of similar factors to those in Bangladesh.

Map	Colours
Figure 3.18	Blue plus purple outline of major river basins
Figure 3.19a	Greens, pink and purples
Figure 3.19b	Blue surrounded by dark green, plus evidence for mountain ranges in the river basins of Figure 3.18

Compare your answer with our 'Comments on activities' towards the end of this book.

The tragedy in Bangladesh and the Indian parts of the Ganges–Brahmaputra plains will undoubtedly focus attention on the problem elsewhere. Activity 3.1 is a crude way of identifying potentially risky areas. There are factors that can contribute to arsenic contamination of drinking water other than those affecting Bangladesh (see comments on Activity 3.1). The only means of properly assessing risk in sufficient detail to take remedial action (Chapter 5) is the systematic chemical testing of groundwater supplies in the areas that emerged from Activity 3.1. However, action in many areas may only follow diagnoses of the clinical signs of chronic arsenic poisoning, as happened in Bangladesh itself.

Summary of Chapter 3

1   Understanding how arsenic came to be released naturally into groundwater beneath the deltaic plains of Bangladesh and adjoining areas begins with the knowledge of how the sedimentary aquifers there were deposited and the effects of sea-level change in such a low-lying area. It also required scientific research into the weathering of debris supplied to the major rivers, and how arsenic was both released to solution from crustal rocks and then adsorbed by iron(III) hydroxide coatings to transported sedimentary grains.

2   The results from research centred on data from the wells themselves, particularly the relationship between dissolved arsenic, well depth and sediment colour. Investigating other ions narrowed down the possible causes to just one: the dissolution of iron(III) hydroxide under reducing conditions.

3   The natural contamination is restricted to distinct zones in Bangladesh underlain by young river sediments that fill deep valleys cut when sea level was lowered during the last Ice Age. Well depths between about 10 m and 130 m penetrate these sediments and are often contaminated. The deepest aquifers contain low arsenic levels.

4   When the sediments were transported and first laid down at the surface, conditions would have been oxidising. Iron(III) hydroxide would have been stable and coated the grains, thereby adsorbing arsenic and other ions. Rapid filling of the valleys as sea level rose in the last 18 000 years trapped organic matter in the sediment. Once oxygen in the sediments had been consumed by

decay, the action of anaerobic bacteria helped iron(III) hydroxide to dissolve, thereby releasing its arsenic content to solution.

5   Anaerobic bacteria that reduce sulfate ions to sulfide can precipitate iron sulfide, which takes up arsenic in reducing conditions. Such bacteria thrive if sulfate ions are concentrated in groundwater, although this is not always the case. This biological activity helps explain spatial association of heavily contaminated wells with those that provide safe water.

6   Chemical analyses of water from many wells spread evenly across Bangladesh show generally how the arsenic hazard varies. Maps derived from the data are not completely reliable, but err on the side of caution. Even in the worst affected areas, some wells do yield safe water supplies.

7   The body of research in Bangladesh provides guidelines to assess large areas elsewhere that might be facing similar hazards.

Water ethics – response and responsibility

Chapter 4

E R

The radio programme *Perfectly Poisoned* that you listened to in Activity 1.1 highlighted the scale of the poisoning disaster in West Bengal, and the inseparable science and societal issues. This chapter will explore the themes of *communication*, *decision making* and, in particular, *ethical issues* in the developing history of drinking water quality in Bangladesh. As you saw in Topic 1, considering ethical issues involves an assessment of 'what should happen' and, in the context of science, this is often very closely linked to risk or 'what could happen'.

The first part of this chapter will consider how the desire to improve access to safe water developed into the crisis of arsenic-poisoned drinking water now faced by the people of Bangladesh. The second part of the chapter examines some of the central themes of ethics and responsibility in the aftermath of the poisoning crisis, including a brief discussion of how the law deals with responsibility for causing unintentional injury and a legal case related to the events in Bangladesh. The final part of this chapter considers the broader context of issues related to water, and future threats to people's access to clean and safe water for domestic and agricultural uses in Bangladesh and globally.

4.1 History of water and well-being in Bangladesh

On first hearing of this mass poisoning in Bangladesh, your immediate reaction is likely to be to ask, 'how and why did this happen?' and 'what should happen now?' These reactions are a normal human response to suffering, and have resulted in an international response to the crisis: offers of aid in the form of scientific expertise to search for the source of the arsenic; expertise to work out ways to extract uncontaminated groundwater (Chapter 3); and funding and scientific expertise to mitigate the arsenic poisoning in groundwater (which you will see in Chapter 5). On a darker note, the reaction to the unfolding crisis has also included investigations, accusations of negligence and poor use of funds. In order to understand some of the issues surrounding the case, we will return to its origins. As you heard in the *Perfectly Poisoned* radio programme on West Bengal, the groundwater resource was exploited in order to alleviate an earlier problem.

E

- ■ What was the reason for drilling thousands of tubewells in the plains of Bangladesh when the country is supplied by two of the largest rivers in the world, the Ganges and the Brahmaputra, and crossed by hundreds of other rivers?

- ■ Prior to drilling the tubewells, in the 1930s and 40s, around 250 000 children in Bangladesh died each year from waterborne diseases such as cholera, typhoid and dysentery. From the 1950s onwards, small numbers of tubewells were drilled to draw water from the ground; this was water uncontaminated by the parasites and bacteria that spread disease.

The tubewells were thus a response to the earlier health crisis caused by highly contaminated surface water and the resulting high infant mortality. The Bangladesh Government began its tubewell project in earnest in 1972, and latterly the international community through UNICEF (United Nations Children's Fund) felt it had a duty to act, to alleviate the huge cost of waterborne diseases affecting people, predominantly women and children, who came into contact with the contaminated water.

E

The question that now arises is why did such a long time (30 to 40 years) elapse between the identification of the issue of waterborne disease and the actions taken to resolve the crisis? Tubewells are not a new technology and had been popular in India for decades before major projects began in Bangladesh. This seems an extraordinary length of time compared to the health issue you considered in Topic 1: BSE was first identified in late 1984, formally recognised as a disease in cattle in 1986, and all brain and spine offal, the main carrier, was removed from the food chain three years later in 1989, several years before the formal link was established between BSE and vCJD in 1996.

■ How many children in total may have died from waterborne diseases as a result of apparent inaction and delay in improving the quality of drinking water in Bangladesh?

▨ According to the figures above, between 7.5 and 10 million children died in the 30–40 year interval.

From the portrayal above it might seem pertinent to ask whether the British administration of India (until 1947), the Government of Pakistan (1947 to 1971), successive Bangladesh Governments, or international agencies were responsible for the delay. However, it is impossible to separate the issues of deaths resulting from waterborne disease from the history of conflict, drought, flood and famine in what is now Bangladesh.

The land of Bangladesh is mostly made up of alluvial soils formed from old deltaic deposits laid down by rivers draining the Himalaya (Figure 3.6a). This rich soil, combined with the local monsoon climate, make the area an ideal place to grow rice and many cash crops. However, the reliance on agriculture means the society is subject to both feast and famine, depending upon the vagaries of the climate and, in particular, the East Asian monsoon. In addition, the land has to be farmed in order to support the high density of people, so events that cause the population to uproot (including war, drought and flooding) can very quickly have devastating effects despite the fertile land. In fact the area that is now Bangladesh has a long history of famine (Box 4.1). In the time since WWII, Bangladesh has suffered severe droughts in 1951, 1973, 1975, 1978–79, 1981, 1982, 1989 and 1994–95, which have resulted in many deaths from starvation; many people were killed in floods in 1954, 1955, 1970, 1974, 1985, 1988 and 1998. There is also a strong link between the worst disasters and war; there were major periods of extreme famine when the effects of drought or flooding were exacerbated by war in 1943 during WWII, and again in 1974–75 in the aftermath of the War of Independence in 1971–72.

Droughts can be caused by climate variations, such as a weak or absent East Asian monsoon, and a late or absent surge in the major rivers from snow melt in the Himalaya. However, floods are equally devastating because much of Bangladesh lies less than 12 m above sea level, making very large areas susceptible to flooding. In September 1998, the country saw some of the worst floods in recorded human history when the Brahmaputra, Ganges and Meghna rivers broke their banks and covered nearly two-thirds of the entire country in water. Some 30 million people were made homeless, although only around 1000 people died. The cause was unusually intense monsoon rains combined with an equally unusual high level of meltwater from the Himalaya that year. Water as a resource for both drinking and agriculture has dominated the ability of the people of Bangladesh to sustain life – little wonder then that the decision makers (including government and aid agencies) saw groundwater as an easy answer.

■ Considering the previous discussion, briefly identify potential causes for the delay in response to the arsenic in drinking water crisis.

■ In the time since WWII, human crises have been dominated by war and several devastating droughts and floods affecting Bangladesh.

The truth is that many more people have died in floods and droughts than from arsenic poisoning. This in no way belittles the crisis of arsenic poisoning, but it does show the government has to manage several other serious public health issues as well as this.

Box 4.1 The British East India Company

During the years 1768 to 1770, Bangladesh (then part of Bengal) suffered one of the worst famines recorded, during which some 10 million people are thought to have died. The area was actually ruled not by government or another nation, but by the British East India Company, which effectively annexed the area after the Battle of Plassey in 1757 and at the Battle of Buxar in 1764, in which the Company's army defeated the local Nawab and his French allies. This was part of a series of conflicts between the two (then) superpowers over the spice and cotton trade in India, and established the British as the primary power in the Indian subcontinent.

Why was a company allowed to rule a nation in the later part of the 18th century?

The British East India Company was acting as a proxy for British Government interests, which in effect conquered the area for commercial gain. This attitude towards Bengal (Bangladesh was then known as East Bengal) was not restricted to the British, but characterised attitudes of European powers towards India and Africa at the time, as resources to be exploited. The Industrial Revolution was beginning in Britain, and scientific and engineering advances fuelled the need for cheap and plentiful resources, most notably cotton that replaced wool in the rapidly mechanising Lancashire mills between 1750 and 1800.

A drought in Bengal caused crop failure in 1768, and again in 1769, leading to widespread and desperate famine by 1770. While the Company was not responsible for the famine, there have been questions about the role of the British East India Company, which continued to raise land taxes and hoard rice – during a famine in which so many people died that large tracts of land returned to jungle and are recorded to have become impassable. Despite this, the Company continued to rule until 1858 when the British Government took control after the rebellion of 1857. It would be nice to think that such behaviour would not be tolerated by the international community today, but the issue of exploitation for commercial gain continues to be the subject of much debate. For example, reports continue to emerge of the use of children and very low wages in the clothing industry in India and Bangladesh, despite media coverage.

Bangladesh is a young nation, gaining independence first from the British as part of the partition of India and Pakistan in 1947, and latterly independence from Pakistan (which in 1947 was created as two separate areas, West Pakistan and East Pakistan, separated by over 1000 km of India). The relationship between West and East Pakistan deteriorated following partition as the richer and less-populous West Pakistan tried to homogenise the two branches of the country, culminating in a revolt and War of Independence in 1971. The new nation of Bangladesh was established in 1971 as a democracy. From 1971 onwards there was a very strong drive by the government to improve the quality of life for people in Bangladesh as rapidly as possible, to counteract many years of perceived suppression by the British and, latterly, West Pakistan. However, democracy was superseded by one party rule, followed by several army-led coups, before democracy was re-established in 1990. The return of democracy probably reflected changing influences and priorities in the international community at the end of the Cold War.

■ Considering the previous discussion, give two factors that may have contributed to the delay in response to the arsenic in drinking water crisis.

■ The political upheaval and changes since independence in 1971 will almost certainly have contributed significantly to uncertainty over policy. Initially, the new government had to establish many of the tools of state such as ministries for education and health. Subsequently, each regime change entailed a period of uncertainty, a change in the individuals making the policies, and sometimes changes in priorities.

To summarise this section, the history and background to the arsenic poisoning crisis are crucial to understanding what went wrong, and how the people of Bangladesh came to have exchanged high infant mortality through waterborne disease for slow poisoning by high arsenic concentrations in a quarter of the 10 million tubewells. Tubewells in Bangladesh were typically owned and used by small groups, but funded by government and international agencies. From the point where war ceased to be a barrier to development, the imperative to improve people's lives was so strong, and the need for development of safe water so desperate, that the project proceeded extremely rapidly across the whole of Bangladesh with the first 900 000 wells funded by UNICEF, and later funding coming from the World Bank, so that there are now nearly 10 million tubewells. The local-based technology used to drill shallow wells (Figure 1.1c) meant little infrastructure was required, a big advantage given the situation, but this lack of infrastructure also meant there was little or no surveying, no drilling of test wells, and no water quality monitoring. Much of Bangladesh is built on ancient river sediments (Figure 3.6a), so shallow tubewells yield water even when some of the basic understanding of the distribution and yields of aquifers is lacking. Much of the research on their vulnerability has taken place in hindsight, resulting in a huge programme of testing nearly 10 million wells; however, this cannot be achieved instantaneously. In the next section we will discuss the issues relating to the expert knowledge and analytical expertise of scientists in international aid.

Question 4.1

Using the information in Section 4.1 and the data in Table 4.1, explain why deaths resulting from famine have been such a feature of Bangladesh history.

Table 4.1   Population, area and population density (2005) for Southeast Asian countries and the UK (for comparison).

	Population/million	Area/km^2	Density/km^2
India	1100	3290×10^3	334
Pakistan	161	796×10^3	202
Bangladesh	153	144×10^3	1063
UK	61	243×10^3	251

Question 4.2

Using information in this book and Figure 4.1:

(a) Describe the variations in life expectancy for men and women in Bangladesh.

(b) Try to account for (i) the trends and (ii) the exceptions to the trends.

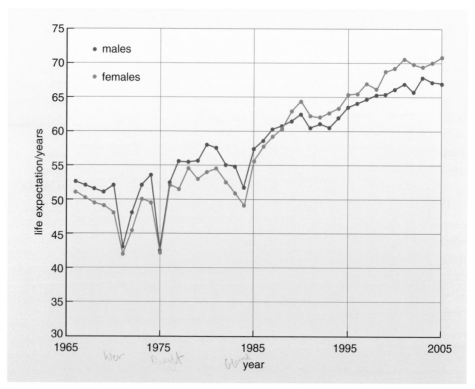

Figure 4.1 Average age at death (also known as life expectancy at birth), based on data from the Matab hospital – now part of International Centre for Diarrhoeal Disease Research, Bangladesh.

4.2 Water ethics and issues of responsibility

Most people would agree that a natural and appropriate response to an issue such as arsenic contamination of the groundwater in Bangladesh is to help the people in the most timely manner possible. A much more difficult question is whether individuals, companies, institutions or countries should carry some level of responsibility for allowing the crisis and deaths of thousands of people to occur, or allowing more people to be harmed by not identifying the crisis earlier. Society encapsulates this issue in the concept of a '*duty of care*', the obligation of a person or group (private company or public body) to avoid acts or omissions that can be reasonably foreseen to be likely to cause harm to others.

Discussion of duty of care in a public health crisis often involves science issues and scientists working closely with decision makers. You have seen a case where ethical issues related to science and decision making played an important role in

Topic 1. In that case, scientists were able to discover a link between animal feed, BSE and, finally, vCJD, and the British Government recognised an ethical responsibility to help victims of the crisis, offering compensation for cattle infected by BSE that had to be slaughtered, and establishing a trust for victims of vCJD. However, scientists also formed part of advisory bodies that considered the contents of animal feeds that allowed the introduction of contaminated animal carcases into the food chain. The British Government responded morally to the crisis by offering help, but there was no admission of guilt on the part of any public body or individual. You might take a cynical view that the mere offering of compensation was an admission of some level of guilt on the part of the government. However, there is very little benefit to identifying a particular group to blame in public health crises such as BSE as there is always a complex interplay of causes and responsibilities. In addition, if one individual or a single group is blamed, that blame can deflect criticism from others closely involved and shift the focus away from changing the system to improve public safety. In fact, blaming someone or something connected with tragedy is a concept so deeply embedded that it has become a common metaphor in English – a scapegoat. The term 'scapegoat' has its origins in Judaism, when a live goat was symbolically burdened with the sins of the people and driven into the wilderness to rid the people of their sins. In ancient Greece, human scapegoats were driven from cities in order to mitigate disasters, but modern societies look for 'causation' as a way to improve the society rather than randomly assigning responsibility.

To make sense of issues of moral responsibility, societies use an agreed set of laws, based on ethics and an obligation for moral behaviour, in order for someone to be accepted as a member of that society. The laws of most countries are very similar, revealing a similar underlying moral code. They also regulate the relationship between the individual and the state – they indicate what is expected of both parties. The behaviour of scientists is governed by the same moral code as other members of society but their behaviour is sometimes scrutinised in great detail, particularly in relation to issues related to human health.

- ■ Name a famous oath encapsulating the 'duty' of members of a profession in relation to human health issues.

- ▨ The Hippocratic Oath is a set of instructions as to the ethical practice of medical practitioners.

The Hippocratic Oath is a code originally thought to have been written down by the Greek philosopher Hippocrates in the 4th century BC, setting out the expected behaviour of a physician (doctor). The oath is not something every new doctor has to swear before first putting on a white coat, but it does encapsulate the behaviour expected of professionals involved in human health, and it exists in many forms with equivalents in many countries. The Hippocratic Oath is a series of statements of expected behaviour that might seem self-evident because they are core to many professions involving science. It includes codes for acting in the best interests of the patient, to the best of their ability, to avoid doing anything that might harm the patient, and adhering to the morals of the community. In legal terms, the Hippocratic Oath sets out the 'duty of care' of the physician in relation to the role. The Hippocratic Oath is relevant but not directly applicable in a broader scientific context because scientists working in areas related to human health may not be working directly with an individual, and would commonly have no direct relationship with the individuals affected. Scientists may be working on health issues, such as BSE, which affect many thousands of people to varying extent rather than individuals (Topic 1), or on science that may only have a distant relationship to human health, such as near-Earth objects (Topic 2).

Scientists are part of a community, and society expects them to exhibit behaviour deserving of the trust in which they are placed. There are two additional concepts that society and the legal system use concerning behaviour associated with a duty of care, and they also have important implications for scientists; these concepts are *reasonably foreseeable* and *proximity.*

E

In scientific terms, a *reasonably foreseeable* outcome can be defined as the extent to which a reasonable person or group could have anticipated the consequences of an action. For example, injury to people is a reasonably foreseeable outcome of developing a new type of bomb. Defining what is not reasonably foreseeable is more difficult since many things are foreseeable in hindsight. A change to the ingredients of animal feeds might have had no reasonably foreseeable consequences at the time, but it could also be argued that it might have been possible to foresee consequences based on knowledge that existed in some quarters of the science of transmissible spongiform encephalopathy (TSE) diseases. In the case of BSE and vCJD, the scientists involved would not have been expected to have the knowledge of such diseases since they were extremely rare and restricted to very special circumstances, such as the disease kuru.

E

The concept of *proximity* is the extent to which consequences of an act are a direct, uninterrupted consequence of the original act, and without which the consequences would not have occurred. Consider the following example. If someone is injured when I throw a cricket ball at them, then I am proximal to that event. I am responsible for the consequences, even if I do not expect the ball to hit them given my lack of prowess with a cricket ball. The alternative to this very close proximity is an event so far removed from the original act that the perpetrator cannot be held responsible for the outcome. The best known example of this is the butterfly effect in chaos theory in which tiny changes in initial conditions together with sensitive dependence can cause a chain of events with large changes in the outcome. The term was coined by Edward Lorenz, an American mathematician, in relation to the huge variations in computer weather prediction caused by very small changes to the input parameters. Lorenz presented a talk to the American Academy of Science in 1972 entitled 'Does the flap of a butterfly's wings in Brazil set off a tornado in Texas?' No one would hold the butterfly responsible for the tornado; in legal terms, it is not *proximal* to the consequences, the tornado. In this case, many more important forces were involved in causing the tornado.

E

A health crisis of the magnitude of arsenic poisoning of drinking water in Bangladesh is bound to involve accusations of culpability, and inevitably scientists have been among those accused because the groundwater was not tested for the complete range of all possible impurities. Some anger has also been directed at the Bangladesh Government for the unregulated manner in which the tubewells were installed. However, the small local companies and villages undertaking the drilling work were largely outside the control of a newly established government in a country recovering from a war of independence, with a very strong imperative to improve the quality of life for the people. It could be argued that the Bangladesh Government had a 'duty of care' to its people, but that it was acting appropriately by providing drinking water from what appeared to be a clean and reliable source, compared with the seasonally variable and often contaminated and disease-ridden surface waters.

Improving water quality through tubewell drilling was not the only initiative undertaken at the time. The government focused on several areas including health education, increasing the number of trained health professionals, and initiating a programme that has built thousands of local and regional hospitals in the last 20 years. The combination of all these programmes has greatly reduced the mortality among young children. However, given its limited capabilities immediately following independence, the government relied upon external aid agencies to help alleviate the waterborne disease crisis.

RED

The Bangladesh Government and UNICEF initiated the rapidly developing tubewells programme in 1972, funding 900 000 tubewells. While the programme involved basic testing, it did not test the arsenic levels in the water. At the time the project was initiated, standard procedures for testing the safety of groundwater did not include tests for arsenic. In many areas of the world, well water (even deep well water) has been used for drinking with no ill effects. However, knowledge of the risks from arsenic did exist in some quarters – particularly with regard to contaminated waste waters from mining activities. Data on arsenic poisoning of well water in Taiwan (See Section 2.3.2) had been published in scientific journals as early as the 1960s. Those studies, and others in Chile and the USA, prompted the US Environmental Protection Agency (EPA) to publish a report in 1988 that emphasised a risk of 1 or 2 people in 1000 contracting cancers from drinking water that contains arsenic levels above 50 μg l^{-1}. The same level was adopted by the European Community in 1980. Arsenic has appeared on the WHO (World Health Organisation) list of hazardous water contaminants since 1984, along with other elements and compounds some of which are shown in Table 2.1. However, Table 2.1 is restricted to 26 elements; if it had including organic compounds known to cause problems in water, it would have extended to over 100 elements and compounds (a number that is constantly under revision) and taken up a significant proportion of this book. Remember that tubewells were not a new technology, nor considered a dangerous enterprise; they were a well-established and standard way to obtain clean water across Asia and, indeed, many other areas of the world. Analysing for every potential hazard on the list would require a constant programme of analysis and re-analysis. This level of testing was not undertaken at the time, even in the developed nations, unless there was prior indication of a problem, such as the potential for contamination by mine waste. Scientists working with UNICEF, in this case experts in public health, made assumptions about the groundwater based on existing knowledge, but, in hindsight, the assumptions turned out to be invalid. The question of *duty of care* and whether the arsenic poisoning crisis could have been *reasonably foreseen* has been considered in a legal case that arose from a small parallel project.

In August 2002, a claim for substantial damages was issued in London by lawyers on behalf of one of about 400 potential claimants from Bangladesh. This is an example of a class action (a lawsuit brought by one plaintiff on behalf of a large group of others who have a common interest), the success of which would establish a precedent for other members of the group to take similar actions. The actual claimant was Mr Binod Sutradhar, who claimed against the British Geological Survey (BGS) and the Natural Environment Research Council (NERC). The origins of the claim stem from a small project funded by the then Overseas Development Agency (ODA) of the UK Government (now the Department for International Development (DfID). Between 1983 and 1992, the ODA funded a project to drill 4000 tubewells for agricultural purposes (mainly irrigation and fish farming) north of the city of Dacca, Bangladesh. In 1984, the ODA commissioned the BGS to undertake hydrogeological work with a view to testing the efficiency of different tubewell designs, a project that was completed in 1988. Using a small amount of funding remaining at the end of that project, a second project was undertaken to check for deterioration of the wells between 1991 and 1992 and a further report was produced. Crucially, the second project included some analyses of the well water in order to test for deficiency of iodine and high concentrations of iron, phosphorus and zinc that could be harmful to fish (fish farming was being developed in the area), but the project did not measure the concentration of arsenic. The report ended with a proposal for additional work:

> This type of rapid reconnaissance survey produces information of relevance not only to hydrogeologists but also to those who are concerned with availability and quality of groundwater for domestic, agricultural, aquaculture and industrial usage. Similar studies undertaken in other parts of Bangladesh could produce comparable results given limited hydrogeological inputs.

> Hydrochemical character of the main aquifer units of central and northeastern Bangladesh and possible toxicity of groundwater to fish and humans, 1992

Mr Sutradhar was one of the people affected by arsenic in his drinking water and lived in the area studied by the BGS. He drank pond water until about 1983, when a tubewell was sunk in his village. He then drank groundwater, and had developed symptoms of arsenic poisoning (melanosis, keratosis, and foot ulceration) by 1991. The claim alleged that BGS had caused or materially contributed to Mr Sutradhar's illness by failing to draw attention to the presence of arsenic in his drinking water, or by issuing a report that misrepresented that his water was safe to drink. The central question was whether BGS owed Mr Sutradhar and others in the area a 'duty of care' to test whether the water contained arsenic or, by issuing a report, had given the impression that testing for arsenic was unnecessary.

■ There was a great deal of discussion on the important consequences of the Sutradhar vs NERC case for international aid at the time, and in particular the implications for the provision of scientific expertise as part of international aid efforts. What do you think might have been the issue?

■ If international agencies have a 'duty of care' towards entire nations of people for all the possible consequences of the aid, they would be liable for enormous sums of money that they simply could not afford. It is very likely that aid would be severely reduced because the agencies would not be able to afford the insurance costs.

Ultimately, the case reached the House of Lords, the highest court in the United Kingdom, which hears cases where significant points of law are questioned. In such cases, five House of Lords judges (known as Law Lords) consider the case and, in the case of Sutradhar vs NERC, they unanimously determined that the case was 'hopeless', in other words, it had no prospect of success. The Law Lords' judgement ran to some 20 pages, and referred to decisions in several other preceding cases (precedents) that shed light on the ethical issues of the case.

Referral to earlier cases as the Law Lords did in Sutradhar vs NERC is part of the process of developing the 'common law'. In this case, the Law Lords considered that the BGS did not have a 'duty of care' because they were not in close proximity with the people of Bangladesh who had been injured by arsenic in their water. The Law Lords decided that BGS should not be held responsible for the arsenic poisoning disaster because their actions were so far removed from the crisis and that the cause of the crisis lay elsewhere. In relation to testing for arsenic, the Law Lords wrote:

> "BGS therefore owed no positive duties to the government or people of Bangladesh to do anything. They can be liable only for things they did and the statements they made, not for what they did not do."

The Law Lords also dismissed the claim that the report, by making no mention of arsenic, lulled the people and Government of Bangladesh into a false sense of security. In this regard, they said:

> "The report does not say why they did not include arsenic in the suite of elements for which they ran tests. But the highest that the matter can be put for the claimant is that the absence of a test for arsenic impurities implies that BGS (like it seems, everyone else at the time, including government, UNICEF and those closely involved in the drinking water programme) thought that the presence of arsenic was so unlikely that it was not necessary to test for it. The report can therefore at best be regarded as an implied statement by BGS that they shared that belief."

Even though the Law Lords' words refer to the BGS, it is clear they believed, on the basis of the evidence, that scientists in the Bangladesh Government Service and UNICEF should not be held responsible for the arsenic poisoning crisis either, because the events were not reasonably foreseeable at the time. In other words, their conduct was that expected of a reasonably prudent person or group acting under similar circumstances. The degree of responsibility of individuals or groups of scientists for outcomes following a scientific study, or new science-based technology, is a recurring theme you will meet in several areas of science. The potential for scientists to seek to foresee (predict) hazard is a very important activity, and drilling tubewells in developed countries is often accompanied by water quality testing to very high standards; yet such studies are not and should not be expected to be completely infallible – they are judged by the same criteria as other activities undertaken in the service of society, giving highest weight to protecting people when decisions have to be taken in the light of incomplete, partial or contested knowledge.

■ What is the guiding principle you met earlier in the course that sets out the balance between progress and public safety in order to inform decision making based on scientific data?

■ The Hippocratic Oath is one set of codes intended to inform the behaviour of physicians, but the 'precautionary principle' you met in the *Introduction to the Course* is more applicable to a broad range of science issues relating to public health and well-being.

The high concentration of arsenic in tubewell water in Bangladesh is the focus of this topic, but it is by no means the only water-related issue facing Bangladesh or the rest of the world. In the following section we will briefly cover some of the other issues.

4.3 The global context of water ethics

ED

Water is the ultimate renewable resource; it is rapidly recycled through the global water cycle and cannot easily be destroyed or lost from the Earth. However, three-fifths of the Earth's surface is covered by water, so why is access to clean water such an issue? Well, firstly, we cannot drink 97% of the water at the surface because it is seawater (and therefore undrinkable). Seawater is extremely expensive and inefficient to purify, although desalination is undertaken in desert countries such as Saudi Arabia. Of the remaining water (i.e. 3%), around two-thirds is locked up in ice close to the North and South Poles, and most of the remaining water is actually in rock reservoirs, filling pore spaces in a similar way to oil and gas reservoirs, but often it is closer to the surface. Only around one-sixth of the Earth's liquid freshwater is in rivers and lakes. So you can see why the giant reserves of underground water are a tempting target for populations that are short of water, or for whom surface water contains dangerous waterborne parasites and diseases. Crucially, water reservoirs in rocks take time to replenish and, in some areas of the world, they are being emptied faster than they are being replenished. In some extreme cases, humans are emptying closed reservoirs (rock reservoirs that were filled when the climate was wetter) and which are not being replenished at the present day. In effect, they are mining a limited resource in a similar way to the way in which oil or natural gas are mined. In Bangladesh, however, the underground reservoirs are being replenished by freshwater in the Himalaya and by rainfall during the monsoon.

The truth is that human management of water is the issue, rather than the presence or lack of water. The ethics of this situation are clear – there has to be a global response aimed at providing sustainable access to clean water. However, as with the issue of climate change that you will meet as a later topic in this course, the actions require funding and, ultimately, decisions by the international community to change the way we do things, because the current system is depleting water resources and has the potential to reduce the quality of life globally as some of the examples below demonstrate. To set the discussion of Bangladesh in a global context, we need briefly to explore the themes of water quality, water and agriculture, and water ownership, using a series of real examples. The water quality issues faced by the people of Bangladesh are not unique, indeed they are common.

4.3.1 Water quality

Many would argue access to clean drinking water is a basic human right, in other words it is something that should happen, and most people would consider that it is ethically right to strive for global access to clean water. Indeed, the former UN Secretary General Kofi Annan said:

ED

> We shall not finally defeat AIDS, tuberculosis, malaria and any other infectious diseases that plague the developing world until we have also won the battle for safe drinking water, sanitation and basic health care.

> Kofi Annan (2005)

While mortality resulting from waterborne disease has reduced significantly in Bangladesh over the last few years, according to WHO some 20% of the world's population, mostly in developing nations, do not have access to clean (safe) water for drinking, personal hygiene and domestic use (cooking). Despite the arsenic contamination disaster in Bangladesh, groundwater is the safest source of drinking water for developing countries in Asia and Africa, which still suffer high mortality resulting from waterborne diseases. By 2002, the estimated global mortality rate due to water hygiene-associated diarrhoea was 1.8 million, and an additional 1.3 million deaths were the result of malaria and other waterborne diseases. Waterborne diseases (including malaria) account for around 20% of all deaths in children under the age of five in developing nations.

Malaria is considered along with waterborne diseases since it is exacerbated by poor or dysfunctional drainage systems and stagnant water that become infested with malaria-carrying mosquitoes. To put this in context, malaria is still the biggest killer of children in Africa, although the AIDS epidemic kills more adults. The international community recognises the severe problems in Africa and is attempting to address them in a range of projects. In particular, the UN has a project supplying simple nets for beds, which is intended to halve childhood deaths from malaria in Africa by 2015. The situation in Bangladesh has improved in recent years: infant (less than 1 year old) mortality has reduced from over 100 per 1000 live births in 1983 to less than 50 per 1000 live births in 2008, and is the main reason for the increase in life expectancy seen in Figure 4.1. Despite the arsenic poisoning crisis, improvements in water quality, political stability and childcare have improved the quality of life in Bangladesh.

ED

The issue of clean water has a sufficiently high profile that the United Nations Millennium Development Goals included halving the proportion of people without access to safe drinking water and basic sanitation by 2015. As part of the UN programme, the years 2005 to 2015 have been declared the UN 'Decade of Water', and the UN World Water Assessment Programme reports on progress towards the goals every 3 years (thus far it has been reported in 2003 and 2006).

ED

4.3.2 Water and agriculture

Alongside the issues of water quality for domestic use, the world's water resources are coming under increasing stress as a result of agriculture and, in particular, cash crops such as rice, cotton, and oil seeds, rather than subsistence farming. The reason for this is simple – developing nations need to earn money to pay for infrastructure, one route to which is through large-scale agriculture and cash crops. A reliable water supply through the use of irrigation is the key to growing cash crops and thus large irrigation schemes have been built in developing countries throughout Asia and Africa. Some have been successful, but, unfortunately, many have faltered. Bangladesh has natural and artificial reservoirs of water to last through a normal dry season, but tubewells continue to yield water long after the surface reservoirs have failed in drought years. Much of the water used for irrigation in Bangladesh is thus pumped from tubewells, and is usually used for cash crops such as rice, cotton and tobacco.

The use of water for agriculture is a global issue, and is a major issue in Pakistan, which is Bangladesh's less populous and arid near neighbour. In the days of the British Empire, engineers famously built railways across the Indian subcontinent, but they also built canals for irrigation of vast areas of cash crops. In 1947, there were more miles of canals in the subcontinent than railways, and the greatest concentration was on the Indus Plain, in Pakistan. The Indus has a long history of irrigation close to its banks, but engineers extended its reach by building dams to hold back the spring thaw in the Himalaya and to channel the waters into areas many hundreds of kilometres from the river. After independence, the World Bank funded yet larger dams and irrigation projects, and today half of Pakistan's power is hydroelectric power and 90% of the crops grow on irrigated land.

Several problems stem from Pakistan's dependence upon water from the Indus. First and foremost is the problem of steadily increasing salinity caused by irrigating land with river water or ground water in a very arid environment. In such areas, water evaporates rapidly, leaving an ever-increasing concentration of many salts, in particular NaCl (i.e. common salt), in the soil. The addition of NaCl is the consequence of a fundamental difference between rainwater and other sources of water. Rainwater contains between 0 and 50 μg l^{-1} NaCl, whereas river waters and groundwaters contain between 1000 and 5000 μg l^{-1} NaCl, and, for comparison, seawater contains 35 000 μg l^{-1}. In some areas of Pakistan, the problem is becoming acute and farmers are abandoning fields because there is now so much salt in the soil that it poisons the crops. Around 10% of fields on the Indus Plain have been abandoned so far, and many more are threatened by rising salt levels in the soil. This problem is not restricted to Pakistan and is particularly acute in areas of Australia. While newer salt-resistant strains of rice are being developed, the quality of water for agriculture will continue to be an important issue in Bangladesh even after the arsenic problems have been solved.

4.3.3 Water ownership

If the wars of the 20th Century were fought over oil – the wars of the 21st century will be fought over water.

Ismail Serageidin, Vice President of the World Bank and Founder of the Global Water Partnership, 1995

Dams are built to harness the peak flow of a river for hydroelectric power, irrigation or domestic use throughout the year, and even when the rivers flow through just one country, water abstraction can affect users downstream. When rivers run through more than one country, damming or diverting them becomes an international issue.

The Farakka Barrage is a long dam located on the river Ganges just 10 kilometres inside India, which was completed in 1975. The dam diverts a significant proportion of the Ganges flow into the Hooghly river which runs through India, before it reaches Bangladesh. The main motivation for India to erect the dam was to increase flow in the Hooghly river to prevent silt build-up closing the port of Kolkata in India. A 26 mile canal carries water from the Ganges into the Hooghly river, and withdrawal of water by India has been the source of a long-running dispute between the two countries.

Bangladesh has claimed that excessive withdrawal of Ganges water at Farakka in India over the whole period of its operation has affected not only agriculture but also fishery, navigation, industry and vegetation in the region that comprises around a quarter of Bangladesh. Bangladesh claims that the reduced flow has led to seawater penetration into the river more than two hundred miles inland from the coast, because the Ganges no longer carries enough water to flush its lower reaches into the Bay of Bengal. The dispute reached the UN General Assembly in 1976 and again in 1993.

More recently, and for the people of Bangladesh even more worryingly, China is preparing to build a dam on the Tsang Po river. Figure 3.2 shows the Tsang Po flowing west to east in Tibet (called Xizang by the People's Republic of China), north of the Himalayan mountain chain. The Tsang Po becomes the Brahmaputra as it flows around the eastern end of the Himalaya. The new dam is intended to supply both hydroelectric power and irrigation in the Xinjiang and Gansu portions of the Gobi Desert over 400 miles away. The dispute over this latest proposed dam highlights the importance of the security of water supplies, particularly for a small and relatively poor nation such as Bangladesh. However, the Brahmaputra flows through India for much of its course, and this rapidly developing nation is likely to vigorously dispute water abstraction that affects Indian agriculture and industry. This short case study illustrates the internationalisation of water issues, and the potential future dangers for Bangladesh, which sees huge naturally driven variations in water supply that may in future be vulnerable to human-generated reductions in its water supply.

Summary of Chapter 4

1   Access to clean water in Bangladesh has been a serious health issue for many years, and the use of contaminated surface waters caused around 250 000 deaths a year, predominantly children, in the 1930s and 40s.

2   Water and health issues in Bangladesh are intimately tied up with the history of the country, a history that has included the Colonial Era, independence from Britain, separation from India, independence from Pakistan and, later, regime change. Understanding water and health in Bangladesh also requires an understanding of the population density and climatic conditions, particularly the susceptibility to flooding and drought.

3   Soon after independence from Pakistan the new government in Bangladesh was attempting to improve the standard of living by improving the health of the people by providing access to clean and safe water. Funding from international agencies, such as UNICEF, was used to undertake an intense program of tubewell drilling.

4   Ethical issues arising from a public health crisis, such as the arsenic poisoning of water in Bangladesh, include issues of moral responsibility and may include blame, although assigning blame to a particular individual or group is not helpful and may deflect criticism from other people who are closely involved. The Bangladesh Government had a duty of care towards its citizens over water quality, though it relied on international agencies in the race to improve the quality of life of the Bangladesh people. 'Duty of care' is the obligation of a person or group to avoid acts or omissions that can reasonably be foreseen to be likely to cause harm.

5   Scientists are part of society and are expected to exhibit behaviour deserving of the trust which is placed in them. The Hippocratic Oath is an example of a set of behaviours expected of professionals although it relates to medical practitioners rather than scientists.

6   A class action was brought against NERC and BGS by a group of people in Bangladesh affected by arsenic poisoning as a result of drinking tubewell water, but the Law Lords decided that BGS could not be held responsible for the disaster because their actions were so far removed from the issues surrounding the poisoning.

7   There are many internationally important issues concerning water quality in developing nations with some 20% of the world's population still unable to access clean water.

8   Many of the world's cash crops are now dependent upon irrigation and, as climate changes, these are in increasingly vulnerable low-rainfall areas. Soil salination is becoming an increasingly important issue in areas such as Pakistan.

9   Water ownership and governance is fast becoming a critical international issue. Many of the world's largest rivers run through more than one country, and water extraction in India is already leading to serious problems in Bangladesh.

Chapter 5

Managing and mitigating the problem

Once the scourge of chronic arsenic poisoning in Bangladesh and neighbouring parts of India became widely known in 1995, decisions and action had to be taken at many different levels.

Question 5.1

Note down aspects of the arsenic poisoning crisis where you think crucial decisions would have to be taken and acted upon.

In 1998 the UK's Department for International Development (DfID) funded detailed analyses by MMI and the BGS of most of the wells sunk in the programme initiated by its predecessor, the Overseas Development Administration (ODA), thereby outlining the regional risks (Section 3.4.1). In 1998, UNICEF set up a programme to use a simple low-cost test to check arsenic concentrations in water from every well in Bangladesh, including strengthening the analytical facilities and skills in government water agencies. If a well's water exceeds the 50 µg l^{-1} level, its pump is painted red, while pumps at safer wells are painted green. The red pumps can be used for any purpose other than drinking or cooking. The UNICEF programme also aims to raise awareness about arsenic contamination and its effects, through a communications campaign that accompanies the water testing. Its other aims are to identify people showing typical symptoms, set up an arsenic database, and assist in developing low-cost means of removing arsenic from drinking water. UNICEF's initiative involves progressively transferring responsibility for all aspects of the programme to national agencies. Arsenicosis produces disfiguring symptoms (superficially similar to leprosy) and associated stigma. So a prime requirement for the Bangladesh Government was to convince people that this was not a communicable disease and not everyone would get the symptoms. In 2005, UNICEF's programme and many others had not been completed.

From Sections 2.3.1 and 2.3.2, you should recall that arsenic concentrations of 50 µg l^{-1} cause both skin complaints and cancers, so water with those levels is not safe. Yet, this is the concentration adopted in the 1990s by both Bangladesh and India as the maximum permissible in drinking water. It was also deemed safe by US authorities until 2001, when the limit was lowered to the WHO standard of 10 µg l^{-1}, which became enforceable in 2006.

■ Suggest reasons for what seems to breach an ethical approach to safety in the Indian subcontinent.

■ In Bangladesh and India there are vast numbers of water sources, so it will take time to assess them all. A concentration of 10 µg l^{-1} (10 parts per billion) or less is not easy to measure, as it involves using time-consuming, sophisticated and expensive analytical methods. So the reasons are essentially pragmatic.

The method adopted by UNICEF uses a colour change in a mercury compound that reacts with the gas arsine (AsH$_3$). Adding acid and metal powder to well water released hydrogen. If arsenic is dissolved in the water, hydrogen combines with arsenic ions to produce minute amounts of arsine and a paper strip

(handwritten margin notes:)
D Testing
Medical provision
Public advice
Alternatives
R Financing research

E

impregnated with the mercury compound and suspended above the treated water changes colour. However, at levels below 50 μg l⁻¹ the change is barely noticeable. Nonetheless, for concentrations of 50 μg l⁻¹ and more, the test takes only 20 minutes, at a cost of a few pence, and can be done at the well itself with little training. 'State-of-the-art' analyses that reach below 1 μg l⁻¹ use equipment that cannot be taken to the field. Samples brought to the laboratory can be analysed in about the same time as by the paper-strip method, but even in the USA the pressure on this laboratory method is such that introducing WHO standards required a 5 year programme.

Water analyses that followed adoption of a 10 μg l⁻¹ standard in the USA have revealed that a large number of public water supplies do not meet it. The US Environmental Protection Agency (EPA) has estimated that the annual cost per household of reducing arsenic to below this concentration will be between $30 and $300, for regional water utilities and for those serving less than 10 000 people respectively. In 2005, 6 months before compliance with the new standard becomes obligatory, water supplies to about 13 million people remain above the limit. The Bangladesh Government's annual expenditure in 2003 on *all* public services was $53 per capita, so you can see clearly the economic difficulty of coping with the arsenic tragedy in that country.

At every stage in the story of waterborne arsenic there have been delays for many reasons: technical, as in the case of monitoring; ignorance to a variety of degrees; poor communications of different kinds; the sheer inertia of the decision-making and fund-releasing processes. The remainder of this chapter concerns strategies for mitigating or reducing the effects of the known risks from arsenic.

5.1 Mitigation

Mitigating arsenic contamination is an essential strategy, about which your study of earlier chapters has equipped you to comment with some authority. Unfortunately, ailments that result from long-term exposure cannot be cured by chelation therapy (Section 2.2.1), which can to some extent help people who have been poisoned by a high, single dose. Chronic arsenicosis results from cell or genetic damage of various kinds. Some aspects can be treated, but not cured. It is not known if drinking safe water, once arsenicosis is diagnosed, stops or slows the development of the many conditions that fall under that medical term, particularly the various cancers that appear long after exposure. Nonetheless, provision of safe water is the most vital aspect of mitigation.

Question 5.2

Write down as many ways you can think of that might remove the exposure to risk of people in arsenic-affected areas.

Migration is not a realistic option in a densely populated, poor country like Bangladesh. Having seen the dramatic reduction in death of under-fives after well water supplanted that from surface sources, most Bangladeshis now prefer groundwater, despite the hazard. (You may recall from *Perfectly Poisoned* that it took a great deal of persuasion for people to accept groundwater when the programme of well drilling began in the 1970s, because of their belief that it was 'the devil's water'.) For many, another reason was that one extended family could have their own well, instead of using communal surface supplies. Originally, most villages used rain-fed ponds. Surface water can be rendered safe from pathogens and parasites by filtration through sand beds and disinfection at low to moderate cost, and it would be possible to lessen biological contamination by using roofs for collection and concrete cisterns for storage. Supplying well water from uncontaminated areas is problematic, aside from the cost of pipelines. Effectively, it would *reduce* a resource in more fortunate areas. As the answer to Question 3.3 showed, in those areas where arsenic is a problem in some wells, those deeper than about 150 m have much lower concentrations than the shallower wells. Extending existing contaminated wells to the depth of safe groundwater is an attractive option, but only where the depth of sediment *does* exceed 150 m: in some areas it does not. Although these approaches are being adopted, much effort in Bangladesh and other areas is directed to removing arsenic from water supplied by existing wells.

5.1.1 Water treatment

The Bangladesh tragedy, but also the 2001 decision of the US Government to reduce the enforceable maximum permitted concentration of arsenic in drinking water from 50 µg l⁻¹ to 10 µg l⁻¹ (obligatory by January 2006), has spurred research into an efficient means of removing it from public supplies.

■ Suggest a principle behind at least one possible means of such remediation from your study of Chapter 3.

▨ Iron(III) hydroxide is a natural adsorber of arsenic. It can also purify water contaminated with other toxic metals, such as cadmium and mercury, which also become attached to it.

Iron(III) hydroxide coatings of ordinary sand grains in an oxidised sediment should be capable of removing arsenic from aqueous solution. Red–orange, iron-rich sand is widely available and inexpensive to excavate and transport: most builders' yards have a plentiful supply.

■ Chemically, iron-rich sand should remove arsenic from aqueous solution, but can you think of any limitations?

▨ Its usefulness depends on several factors: the rate of adsorption, the maximum amount of arsenic that can be adsorbed per kilogram of hydroxide before it is 'spent' and whether the adsorbent used can be disposed of safely.

Simple filters (Figure 5.1) that use local iron-rich sand in Vietnam reduce arsenic concentrations from as high as 400 µg l⁻¹ in groundwater to acceptable levels. Even crushed red house bricks are a possible solution, having lessened dissolved arsenic to one-twentieth of its natural level in trials. Some iron ores contain abundant iron(III) hydroxide. In crushed form, they might be efficient purification agents. There is one problem with natural iron(III) hydroxide: namely, having been exposed to circulating water for a long time, some dissolved ions will already have been adsorbed, thereby reducing further uptake of arsenic. Pure iron(III) hydroxide produced by precipitation and made into granules can remove up to 40 g of arsenic per kilogram of the product.

Figure 5.1   Simple arsenic-removal systems. (a) Well in West Bengal fitted with a filter system. (b) Ideal system attached directly to the pump outlet at a well. (c) Filter bed: pumped water first flows through the arsenic-removing filter, then to a storage tank fitted with a settling chamber for fine, suspended material.

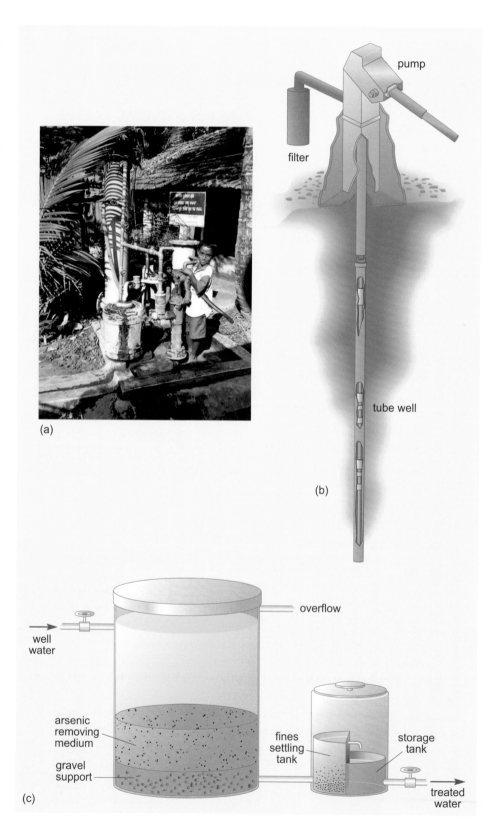

Question 5.3

Assume that the amount of water for drinking and cooking used by one person is about 2000 l y^{-1}. For water contaminated with arsenic at a concentration of 200 µg l^{-1}, how much granular iron(III) hydroxide would be needed to purify this annual supply?

The amount of material is so small that, for a Bangladeshi community of 1000 people using one well, a filter containing only 10 kg of granular iron(III) hydroxide would make their drinking water safe for a year. However, the spent medium would contain 0.4 kg of arsenic to be disposed of safely each year.

■ Would you anticipate problems of arsenic leakage from the spent medium if it came into contact with water?

■ Provided conditions remained oxidising, as they would at the surface, there is no reason to suppose that the iron(III) hydroxide would dissolve and release its adsorbed arsenic.

However, this simple kind of direct filtering takes no account of the *rate* of adsorption. That is important, because a well equipped only with a pump and a filter attached to its outlet (Figure 5.1a) requires the adsorption to occur almost instantaneously. Pure iron(III) hydroxide is used in filter beds where arsenic poses a local problem in Europe, and at least 3 minutes contact is required for efficient arsenic removal. So, to be effective in Bangladesh, granular iron(III) hydroxide would have to be used in some kind of filtration bed at each well. The cost of building such a simple filter is not prohibitive. A 100 l oil drum filled with adsorbent material (Figure 5.1c) through which water from the well pump passes slowly before being collected for use would be a low-cost, effective solution. The same design applies to large-scale filtration systems.

Another way to speed up adsorption is to decrease the grain size of the medium: any reaction between liquids and solids depends on the surface area of the solid reagent (Question 3.1). The smallest particles of a compound are produced when it is chemically precipitated in water. Soluble salts of iron(II), such as its chloride or sulfate, immediately react with oxygenated water to form iron(III) hydroxide. This would definitely increase the rate of arsenic removal, but the precipitated particles are so small that they remain in suspension, making the water red, and of course they would carry arsenic (conditions in our digestive tract are highly reducing, so the iron(III) hydroxide would dissolve and release adsorbed arsenic). So simply adding an iron salt to contaminated water is not a solution, unless it is part of a sophisticated processing plant that involves settling tanks and filtering through sand beds. However, fine-grained iron(III) hydroxide is also produced when metallic iron is allowed to rust. Filters containing iron 'wool' mixed with more stable fibres have been tried at the outlet of well pumps, but eventually the iron becomes completely rusted and the hydroxide can clog the filter or contaminate the filtered water. Such filters would need to be carefully designed and manufactured, thereby adding to cost.

Several other metals produce compounds with arsenic-adsorbing properties, notably aluminium oxide (Al_2O_3), which is the feedstock for aluminium smelting and cheaply available. However, its capacity is only up to 1 g per kilogram of the medium, i.e. 40 times less than granular iron(III) hydroxide. It can be regenerated by washing with dilute sodium hydroxide (caustic soda) solution, but that presents the problem of what happens to the arsenic that has been removed in solution. Remediation in rural Bangladesh seems to be best served by the adsorption strategy using iron(III) hydroxide. But there are other, more sophisticated possibilities to consider.

Synthetic resins have been developed whose structure incorporates common ions that selectively replace those of other ions dissolved in water (Figure 5.2). They are known as **ion-exchange resins**. In the case of arsenic, the most promising resin exchanges chloride ions (Cl^-) for complex arsenate ions (AsO_4^{3-}). Beads of the resin gain a positive charge when they release chloride anions, thereby enabling loose bonding with the arsenate anions. Ion exchange is almost instantaneous, a decided advantage over adsorption processes. Once they become saturated with arsenic after a few months, the resin beads are regenerated by flushing them with sodium chloride (common salt) solution. This process again presupposes a safe means of disposing of the flushed arsenic. Another problem with ion-exchange resins is that other ions in the water also substitute for the chloride ions, for example sulfate ions (SO_4^{2-}) that are common in many natural waters can more than halve the resin's efficiency for arsenic removal. However, the most highly contaminated well waters in Bangladesh have low sulfate contents (Figure 3.9a). Despite their clear advantage over adsorption methods, ion-exchange resins involve complex manufacturing and are more costly.

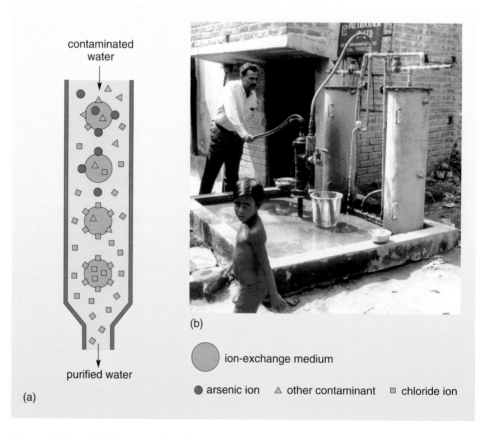

Figure 5.2   (a) Diagram showing how ion-exchange resins work. (b) Village pump in Bangladesh fitted with an ion-exchange system.

In addition to inorganic means of arsenic remediation, several interesting but untested possibilities have arisen from research by biologists.

■ Recall from Chapter 3 one biological means of removing arsenic.

▨ Sulfate–sulfide reducing bacteria living in anaerobic conditions generate hydrogen sulfide. This precipitates iron(II) sulfide, which can take up large amounts of arsenic. You should also recall that such a phenomenon could be responsible for widely varying arsenic concentrations in more generally contaminated shallow wells (Section 3.3).

Samples from wells in a completely homogeneous aquifer in Illinois, USA, show a wide range of arsenic concentrations, ranging from safe to highly contaminated. When attempts were made to culture any bacteria that might be present in each well, microbiologists discovered that water from wells with the lowest arsenic content contained sulfate–sulfide reducing bacteria, whereas they were absent from the most contaminated wells. They concluded that arsenic had been precipitated in sulfide minerals. It may therefore be possible that 'seeding' contaminated wells with sulfate ions might encourage such bacteria to thrive and purify the water. There is a drawback; release of sulfide ions can also generate hydrogen sulfide gas that would make the water evil smelling.

One of the oddest discoveries is that some species of fern may have effective remedial action. Suspending ferns of the genus *Pteris* in water containing arsenic concentrations between 20 μg l^{-1} and 500 μg l^{-1} reduced the highest arsenic concentration to 2.8 μg l^{-1} within a day. Similar results are found with the water hyacinth (*Eichornia crassipes*), which infests many ponds in tropical countries. The problem with using plants, however, is once again disposal. If they are left to rot, anaerobic conditions would release the arsenic to surface water.

Research continues into other arsenic-adsorbent remediation media, including the use of abundant materials such as calcium carbonate (the mineral from which limestones are composed), titanium oxide (the harmless, white base for paints) suspended in water and exposed to sunlight, and even coal ash.

Because the problem of arsenic contamination by the same means as present in Bangladesh has arisen in many other areas, and the tragedy itself has entered the world political scene at the highest levels, remediation is a high priority. The Bangladesh tragedy also brought the hazard of waterborne arsenic to the forefront in many rich countries, helping create increasingly powerful pressure groups. The clearest sign of its impact is the US Government's decision to reduce the maximum tolerable concentration there to one-fifth of its former level. This is fuelling research into both epidemiology and effective remediation technologies at a level matched only by seeking remedies for the HIV/AIDS, malaria and tuberculosis pandemics.

Activity 1.2 (Part 2)
Allow 20 minutes

Compare your own notes on the relevance of material in Chapters 2–5 to the theme of communication with the discussion in 'Comments on activities' towards the end of this book.

Summary of Chapter 5

1   The emergence of the arsenic crisis in Bangladesh required decisions to be made both nationally and internationally, by governments, contractors and humanitarian agencies.

2   It also demanded that the hazard be communicated to the people likely to be affected in ways that were easily understood. As the results of chemical surveys of water came in, they too had to be communicated to authorities able to act on the risks that the data indicated. The most crucial decision, considering the scale of the problem, concerned how to mitigate established ill health.

3   Although there are several possible strategies for making drinking water safe, initiating different options faces several challenges. An important one is establishing the highest permissible arsenic concentration in water supplies. That is problematic in two respects: the *cost* and the *technical difficulties* of evaluating all supplies. Many water users preferred to take the risk of long-term damage from drinking groundwater rather than a return to the immediate risk from diseases carried by surface water.

4   Arsenic can be removed from groundwater by several filtration methods that exploit the surface chemistry of iron(III) hydroxide and other adsorbent compounds, but none take effect immediately. They are best deployed in sand filter beds. Ion-exchange filters are almost immediate in reducing arsenic levels, but must be recharged periodically. All filtration methods, and methods that rely on plants taking up arsenic, face the problem of safe disposal after use. An alternative is to encourage anaerobic bacteria to precipitate arsenic-containing iron sulfide by adding sulfate ions to wells. In poor countries, cost as well as efficacy is of paramount concern.

Learning Outcomes for Topic 3

Kn1 and Kn2 are quite diverse, in that this topic gives you an opportunity to revisit aspects of chemistry and geology that you are assumed to have met in previous studies. They are mainly to do with the chemical consequences of the processes of oxidation and reduction, and the water cycle. New information concerns the roles of sea-level change in sculpting the sedimentary geology of low-lying areas, the stability of simple iron minerals and their surface chemistry, and how they govern the entry of arsenic into aqueous solution. Biological as well as chemical and geological processes are interwoven in the topic, enabling you to visualise the complexity of environmental hazards as well as how this knowledge can be used to help mitigate them. Kn3 to Kn6, which concern the four course themes of communication, risk, ethical issues and decision making in scientific contexts, are distributed throughout the topic. The most revealing feature is that environmental risk concerns location, and therefore the naturally governed probability of exposure, as well as the nature of a hazard and the consequences of exposure to different concentrations of arsenic. This applies to a global range of geological and geographic conditions.

What you have learned from this topic will enable you to address other instances of exposure to natural hazards that involve potentially toxic materials, given appropriate information about them and their distribution (C5). Development of C1, C3 and C4 will be helped by the diversity of information on which you have had to draw in addressing a many-sided phenomenon, while recognising that there are deficiencies in the available information and data.

Ky1 relates mainly to the text of this topic, but includes the audio band *Perfectly Poisoned*. Assessment may include additional material supplied to you from outside the course. There are plenty of opportunities for you to develop Ky2 through both qualitative information contained in simple maps and numeric data about arsenic. As well as helping to reinforce your skills with units and powers of ten, this topic focuses particularly on chemical equations and interpreting graphs that concern the way in which concentrations of arsenic in groundwater relate to other dissolved ions and to simple geology. Some of the questions and activities involve communicating effectively your conclusions from scientific information, and aspects of communication, risk, ethical issues and decision making, to others (Ky4 and 5). It goes without saying that your study of this topic will help you with Ky6.

Answers to questions

Question 2.1

See Figure 2.10. A concentration of 0.05 mg l^{-1} is equivalent to point A. The range 0.2 mg l^{-1} to 0.9 mg l^{-1} is C to D, and that of 1.5 mg l^{-1} is point F on Figure 2.10. The rest of the dose–response curve is estimated by 'joining the dots'. The fatal concentration is unknown, as the symptoms of fluoride excess are debilitating, which might hasten death. As you will see, this uncertainty about the fatal dose is common to all chronic illnesses induced by chemical contamination.

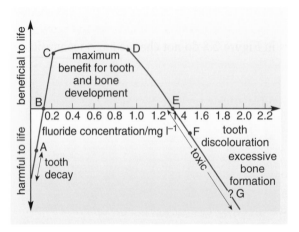

Figure 2.10 Completed dose–response curve for fluoride.

Question 2.2

Lack of access to medical personnel might allow chemically induced ailments to go undetected. Funds may not be available to monitor water quality. Likewise, it may not be possible to improve water quality where it is known to present hazards. In rural areas, people often depend on a single water supply, such as a well, and cannot easily escape any adverse effects, *even if they know about them*. Generally, lower levels of health and nutrition might make people more susceptible to chemically induced ailments than they are in more developed parts of the world: *lower* concentrations than those in WHO guidelines might therefore be more appropriate.

Question 2.3

(a) In arsine gas, As must balance a +3 charge on the three hydrogens, so is in its −3 state; (b) AsO_3^{3-} arsenite ions have a −3 charge and, since three oxygens have −6, As is in a +3 state; (c) in the arsenate ion AsO_4^{3-}, the As must be in a +5 state, because three negative charges from the oxygen are unbonded, leaving −5 with which As is bonded.

Question 2.4

(a) There are incidences of both conditions (skin keratoses and abnormal skin pigmentation) at concentrations of 50 μg l^{-1} or less, so the maximum level adopted for Bangladesh cannot be regarded as safe. (b) The key to the length of exposure is to look at the youngest age group in which either condition has been diagnosed. Under-9s do show both conditions at a range of concentrations, so effects of arsenic poisoning appear after exposures of less than 9 years. It is also noticeable that people older than 10 years are more likely to develop the symptoms. However, the rate at which symptoms do occur may not be exactly the same for young children as for adults. (c) There are quite striking differences between genders, with females of all ages and at all concentrations seemingly being less susceptible, with a few exceptions. One possible reason is that males are more likely to do more heavy manual work outside in a hot country. They would then drink more water on average than women. A test for that would be to ask every individual how much water they drink on average each day.

Question 2.5

All the plots show a regular increase in consequences with exposure expressed as arsenic concentration. The slopes of the graphs in Figure 2.9 and of lines that link the tops of the histogram bars in Figure 2.8 do not change as concentration increases. This is a linear response to exposure, although not perfect – the data points and histogram bars do not fit straight lines exactly. Nevertheless, it would be possible to predict the consequences for broad ranges of arsenic concentrations, if the number of people remained the same. If populations changed, prediction would become more complicated.

Question 3.1

(i) The 1 mm grain has a surface area of

$$4\pi \times 10^{-3} \text{ m} \times 10^{-3} \text{ m} = 4\pi \times 10^{-6} \text{ m}^2$$

and a volume of

$$\frac{4\pi}{3} \times 10^{-3} \text{ m} \times 10^{-3} \text{ m} \times 10^{-3} \text{ m} = \frac{4\pi}{3} \times 10^{-9} \text{ m}^3$$

So the surface area exposed to chemical reaction relative to grain volume is

$$\frac{4\pi \times 10^{-6} \text{ m}^2}{\frac{4\pi}{3} \times 10^{-9} \text{ m}^3} = 3 \times 10^3 \text{ m}^{-1}$$

(Note the 4π on the top and bottom of the equation cancel.)

For the 0.1 mm grain, the surface area is

$$4\pi \times 10^{-4} \text{ m} \times 10^{-4} \text{ m} = 4\pi \times 10^{-8} \text{ m}^2$$

and the volume is

$$\frac{4\pi}{3} \times 10^{-4} \text{ m} \times 10^{-4} \text{ m} \times 10^{-4} \text{ m} = \frac{4\pi}{3} \times 10^{-12} \text{ m}^3$$

So the surface area exposed to chemical reaction relative to grain volume is

$$\frac{4\pi \times 10^{-8} \text{ m}^2}{\frac{4\pi}{3} \times 10^{-12} \text{ m}^3} = 3 \times 10^4 \text{ m}^{-1}$$

Surface area relative to volume is therefore 10 times greater in the smaller grain than in the larger one.

(ii) The smaller grain would therefore decompose 10 times faster than the larger one.

Question 3.2

River water is well oxygenated, especially when it flows turbulently, and so too is the groundwater that seeps into newly deposited river sediments. Equation 2.5 shows that pyrite reacts exothermically with oxygen and water, decomposing to insoluble iron(III) hydroxide and dissolved ions. Given that it takes thousands of years to build up 100 m or so of alluvial and deltaic sediment, most pyrite grains will have been broken down so that elements contained in them will have entered solution. So the answer is no, the pyrite grains are not the source of arsenic pollution.

Question 3.3

(a) No. There are many wells whose arsenic concentrations are below 10 μg l^{-1}. (b) Figure 3.8a shows the greatest clustering of wells with arsenic concentrations above 10 μg l^{-1}, including values over 1000 μg l^{-1}, at well depths between about 10 and 150 m. A much greater proportion of deep wells contain low arsenic concentrations than do shallower ones. (c) The pattern of decreasing incidence of high arsenic values with increasing well depth seems to occur throughout the country (but see Section 3.4). However, for the special study areas (Figure 3.8b), the most risky wells are those shallower than 50 m, whereas the risky depth range is a lot broader across the whole of Bangladesh.

Question 3.4

(a) Wells between 10 m and 150 m deep on Figure 3.8a are most affected by arsenic, and correlate with the zone dominated by grey sediments that contain little iron(III) hydroxide. In the top 35 m of Figure 3.9 there are orange sediments interlayered with grey ones. The worst arsenic contamination occurs in wells that penetrate between 20 m and 50 m, which is above and just below the thin layer of peat at a depth of about 43 m in Figure 3.9. (b) Figure 3.5a shows schematically that peats can occur at several depths, which might account for the wider zone of depths for arsenic-contaminated wells across the whole country. The link in Figure 3.8a between high arsenic concentrations and well depths down to 150 m could indicate that the sediments filling the deepened channels, which formed during the last glacial period, are prone to arsenic contamination.

Question 3.5

Under oxidising conditions, pyrite undergoes the reactions shown in Equations 3.2 and 3.3, so iron in the sediments would be in the form of yellow–brown iron(III) hydroxide. The grey sediments indicate reducing conditions, which are confirmed by the presence of dead organic matter, such as the peats. The yellow–brown sediments coloured by iron(III) hydroxide indicate oxidising conditions.

Question 3.6

The data convincingly refute the hypothesis. Since pyrite oxidation would release sulfate ions, an increase in dissolved arsenic should be matched by an increase in sulfate ions. On Figure 3.10a, the highest arsenic levels are associated with low sulfate ion concentrations. Similarly, pyrite oxidation would increase acidity. The pH of groundwaters lies between 6.5 and 7.5, and the highest arsenic concentrations are associated with pH above 7, i.e. slightly alkaline.

Question 3.7

(a) There are two zones of high phosphate concentrations in wells: down to 150 m, and between 250 m and 350 m. There is a zone of low phosphate between 150 m and 250 m. The zone nearest the surface shows a vague but discernible decrease in phosphate with depth. (b) Based on their phosphorus content, there are two distinct types of groundwater: an upper one that might indicate seepage of fertilisers, and a deep one in which high phosphate is probably due to natural causes, such as varying amounts of calcium phosphate. (c) Evidence from the upper zone that is prone to arsenic contamination could indicate that phosphate substitution for arsenic is occurring in iron(III) hydroxide. That might explain the arsenic contamination in the wells about 35 m deep, where there are some orange, oxidised sediments. However, below that is the zone of iron(III) hydroxide-free sediments that also yields arsenic-contaminated water: the substitution cannot be occurring there. Sediments below about 130 m are stained orange (Figure 3.9) because of iron(III) hydroxide, yet the high phosphate is having no noticeable effect on arsenic concentration, which is below the WHO recommended upper limit.

Question 3.8

The variation of arsenic with dissolved iron(II) (Figure 3.12a) reveals higher Fe concentrations at low concentrations of As and vice versa. So iron concentration does not support the hypothesis. However, there is a clear positive correlation of Mo with As, thereby supporting the hypothesis.

Question 3.9

(a) Most of the areas of *marsh clay and peat* on Figure 3.15b are associated with high arsenic concentrations, but some are not. On Figure 3.6a, those sediments occur in the subsiding Sylhet Basin and in areas being eroded today. The two clay units on Figure 3.15b (the *Barind* and *Madhupur Clays*) are consistently associated with low arsenic concentrations. On Figure 3.6a, both of these clays occur in areas that were not eroded during the last glacial maximum or recently. *Alluvial* and *deltaic* sediments, which are exposed at the surface today, are sometimes associated with high arsenic concentrations, and sometimes not. The other sediments that consistently have low associated arsenic concentrations are *beach sands* and the *alluvial fans* in the northwest. You probably concluded that there is no clear relationship between surface geology and arsenic in well water. (b) The channels eroded at the last glacial maximum below the present courses of the three main rivers are all associated with arsenic contamination to some extent. Areas that underwent no erosion about 20 000 years ago have low arsenic concentrations in well waters. There are areas with high arsenic concentrations in the main belt of contamination that lie outside the buried channels, where erosion proceeds today.

Question 3.10

Well A is *not* contaminated. This is because it penetrates to a level below the peat, where anaerobic bacteria that encourage dissolution of iron(III) hydroxide and release of arsenic have insufficient dead vegetable tissue to thrive. Well B is likely to be contaminated as it draws groundwater from within the organic-rich layer where iron(III) hydroxide will be dissolved. Well C draws water and bacteria upwards from the organic-rich layer, and may be contaminated, especially if pumping is excessive. Well D is in the aerated zone where conditions are oxidising, so iron(III) hydroxide is stable and water will have low arsenic. Well E penetrates sediment in which peat is locally absent, and is therefore safe, despite being in the reduced zone of saturation.

Question 3.11

Factors that have contributed to arsenic contamination in Bangladesh	Topographic and climatic features that may lead to arsenic contamination
Incision of valleys up to 120 m deep in coastal regions when sea level was low during glacial periods	The present elevation must be close to sea level (*all* coastal areas drained by large rivers suffered some incision during the last glacial maximum)
Rapid supply of sediment from mountains	Presence of mountainous areas with high rainfall in river basins, which contribute flow to rivers
Burial of organic matter that creates reducing conditions in the sediments, helping to dissolve iron(III) hydroxide	Humid climate so that coastal areas have luxuriant vegetation, rapid sedimentation.

Question 4.1

Table 4.1 shows that while Bangladesh is a small country (roughly the same size as England), it is home to 150 million people and so has a population density four times that of the United Kingdom. There are over 1000 people per square kilometre, in comparison with about 200 for Pakistan and less than 350 for India. Bangladesh society is still dominantly supported through agriculture, and thus annual crop yields. The extremely high density of people, much higher than for any of the other countries shown in Table 4.1, demonstrates the potential of the area to support people, with both plentiful high-quality soil and silt washed down from the Himalaya, and sufficient water from the East Asian monsoon. However, in order to support such a high density of people, agriculture must be intense, and maintenance of high agricultural output is very dependent upon other factors including climate and political stability. If just one of the factors fails, the results can become devastating very quickly. Thus Bangladesh is very sensitive to climate variation, feeding many people from its own reserves one year, but far fewer in another year. The result is that any significant reduction in agricultural production is sadly associated with potential famine.

Question 4.2

You might make several valid observations from the variations on the life expectancy curve by matching the curve with dates in the text concerning the political and climate history of Bangladesh.

(a) Life expectancy generally increases from low 50s in 1965 to 65–71 years by 2005. In the early years, men live on average 1–2 years longer than women, a trend which reverses around 1988, and by 2005 women live on average 4 years longer than men. There are three departures from this generally increasing trend, two very sudden and significant dips from around 50 years to 42 years in 1971 and 1975, and a more general reduction from around 55 years to 50 years between 1980 and 1984.

(b) The general increasing trend mirrors international changes over the same period and is related to improved sanitation and healthcare, particularly improvements in the healthcare of women and children brought about by increased numbers of local hospitals and healthcare professionals. Improvements in water quality have also improved the quality of life for women and children, though the arsenic poisoning has been a terrible consequence of the rush to improve access to clean water by drilling tubewells.

The reason for men having longer life expectancy than women before 1988 was probably dominated by the greater likelihood of women dying from waterborne diseases since they had responsibility for water carrying and domestic tasks such as cooking and childcare. Since then, the figures approach the norm for other countries, with women tending to live longer then men.

In 1971, many people were killed in the War of Independence, causing the sudden drop in life expectancy. However, many more people died in the resulting famine when the disorder and devastating disruption caused by the war reduced agricultural output, and the huge migration of refugees (many into India) caused a humanitarian crisis. Life expectancy recovered in the following years, only to suffer again due to famine in 1974–5. Although the main reason was probably droughts in 1973 and 1975, the problems were exacerbated by the political situation. The transport infrastructure and inability of the government to buy grain to feed people when the land flooded in 1974 exacerbated the situation. In the years between 1980 and 1985, the situation slowly degraded; although the usual problems of drought and flood continued, it seems likely that political uncertainty and several regimes changes contributed to lack of development.

Additional information not included in the book: From 1985 onwards, life expectancy rapidly rose to the norm for Asia, and in the late 1980s life expectancy for women overtook that for men, in common with many other societies in Asia and the rest of the world. This change reflected improved health care in communities, less waterborne disease, and perhaps an improvement in the quality of life for women in society. The gradual improvement in life expectancy to the present day reflects mainly improved local health care and mirrors the worldwide increases in life expectancy. The global averaged life expectancy is currently 67 years.

Question 5.1

You might have thought of the following: warning people at risk – that requires knowledge of which wells pose a hazard, and therefore comprehensive, accurate analyses; recognising people who have been affected – that requires training paramedics in the symptoms; educating people about the problem – that requires removing the stigma of arsenicosis, and a great deal of care to avoid panic; better understanding of the conditions that encourage arsenic to enter groundwater – that requires more scientific research; finding means of either removing arsenic from water or alternative, safe sources; deciding what the safe limit really is – perhaps the hardest task of all. This is not an exhaustive list.

Question 5.2

You might have thought of the following: migration to unaffected areas; a return to drinking surface water after treatment for biological contaminants; piping in water from unaffected areas; using groundwater from the deep aquifers where oxidising conditions prevail (Chapter 3); somehow removing arsenic from existing groundwater supplies.

Question 5.3

2000 l of contaminated water would contain 400 000 μg of arsenic, or 0.4 g. 1 kg of granular iron(III) hydroxide will remove up to 40 g. So removing 0.4 g requires 10 g of the filter material.

Comments on activities

Activity 1.2 (Part 2)

Table 2.1 (pages 14–15) shows the concentrations in drinking water for several elements that the WHO deem to be the maximum limits for safe consumption. Clearly, these concentrations need to be communicated widely to, for example, agencies responsible for public health and to those who professionally analyse representative samples of drinking water. Similarly, the symptoms of continual ingestion of water above these limits (and any symptoms of element deficiency) should be known by any medical personnel engaged in surveys of general health issues in a population.

The outward symptoms of arsenicosis (pigmented spots on skin and keratoses) are easily recognised (page 29), provided they are communicated to potential victims. Moreover, their superficial resemblance to lesions associated with leprosy can lead to stigmatisation of victims, which is another vital reason for disseminating easily understood information to the general population of an affected area.

In Section 2.3 you worked with actual data on arsenic concentrations in drinking water and considered the likelihoods of various ailments stemming from different ranges of concentration. Clearly, this information is a subject for formal scientific communication to help others assess data from different areas of contamination. However, you may have considered that more general communication of such scientific studies can involve ethical issues faced by medical professionals. For example, on the one hand it might be said that 'everyone has a right to know their fate', yet on the other hand such information might have a range of social repercussions, if it was not fully understood. Communication has to be designed carefully to suit its audience.

The breakdown of iron sulfide (page 50) produces distinctive coloration of material in the banks of streams. Oxidation of sulfides can release toxic metals, so it is important to inform the people that they must not drink water from streams that show such coloration in their banks.

Section 3.3 dealt with the empirical evidence regarding geological attributes associated with arsenic contamination of groundwater. It highlighted four conditions (page 56) that are of especial concern in unconsolidated sediments: shallow depths (<120 m), grey sediments, presence of partly decayed vegetation and anaerobic conditions (evidenced by methane emissions from wells). Such conditions, being easily recognisable by lay people such as well drillers, would be useful as subjects of public communication in areas at general risk.

Applying the understanding gleaned from analysis of the conditions underlying arsenic contamination of Bangladeshi well waters to other parts of the world (Section 3.4.2) depends on formal scientific communication. This could be for example through articles in journals or by disseminating guidelines on an institution-to-institution basis.

There is a good example of clear communication at the beginning of Chapter 5 (page 89) concerning the colour coding of pumps installed at wells in Bangladesh.

It seems incumbent on the Bangladesh Government and UNICEF to mount major public information campaigns (page 89) aimed at countering the stigma associated with arsenicosis, and generally raising awareness about the problem and solutions to it.

Activity 3.1

Several coastal areas in Southeast Asia, such as Myanmar (Burma), Thailand, Cambodia, southern Vietnam and Borneo, may be prone to arsenic contamination. The delta plains of China's major rivers also satisfy the criteria (see answer to Question 3.11). Large parts of coastal Africa and Arabia are either too high or too arid, but the deltas of the Nile, the Niger and Congo rivers are close to sea level and may have problems with arsenic contamination. Parts of the western USA, the Gulf of Mexico and Atlantic coasts of the USA are indicated by the criteria and are potentially contaminated areas. In South America, the Amazon and Parana Basins (eastern Brazil, Paraguay and coastal Argentina) seem threatened, as too do the smaller basins of Venezuela and the Guyanas. Most of northern Eurasia does not show coincidences, for climatic reasons. However, the 'Low Countries' and the delta plains of the Rhine, the Po in northern Italy and that of the Garonne north of the Pyrenees could be arsenic-prone.

Compare your findings from Activity 3.1 with Figure 3.21, which shows areas where arsenic-contaminated groundwater is known to occur. Several of these areas should match your findings, particularly in East Asia, the western USA, Mexico and Argentina. However, other areas do not follow the factors associated with Bangladesh. The area in northern Chile is very dry, but drainage into it is from a major mining area in the high Andes that may have introduced polluted water into unconsolidated sediments. The occurrences in Hungary and Romania are in a sedimentary basin that is too small to show on Figure 3.19. The areas in northwest China and Mongolia seem very different, being cold, high plains surrounded by mountains, but arsenic contamination there involves drainage from mountains into closed basins that are floored by swamps. Conditions exist there for rapid burial of organic matter in the basin sediments, the same processes as in low-lying delta plains. Potentially high-risk areas in South America, such as the Amazon Basin and those of rivers draining Venezuela and the Guyanas, have yet to be investigated.

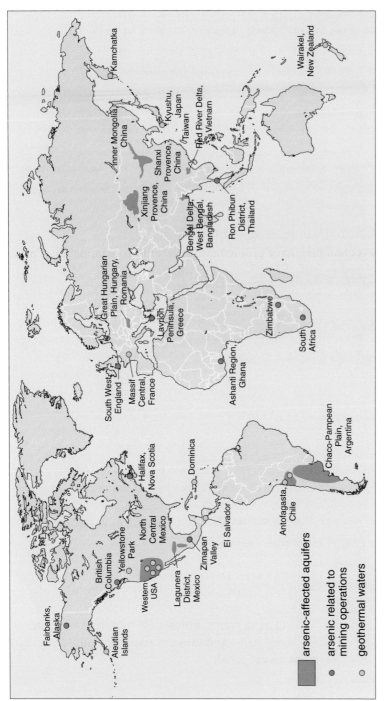

Figure 3.21 Known occurrences of arsenic-contaminated groundwater (2004).

References and further reading

British Geological Survey (1989) *Trace Element Occurrence in British Groundwater*, Research Report SD/89/3.

Chakraborty, A. K. and Saha, K. C. (1987) Arsenical dermatosis from tubewell water in West Bengal, *Indian Journal of Medical Research*, **85**, pp. 326–34.

Chakraborty, A. K., Ghose, A., Gupta, J. D., Chakraborty, D. P., Dey, S. B. and Chattopadhyay, N. (1988) Chronic arsenic toxicity from drinking tubewell water in rural West Bengal, *Bulletin of the World Health Organization*, **66**(4), pp. 499–506.

Davies, J. and Exley, C. (1992) *Short term pilot project to assess the "Hydrochemical character of the main aquifer units of central and northeastern Bangladesh and possible toxicity of groundwater to fish and humans", Final Report*, BGS Technical Report WD/92/43R and Supplement WD/92/44R, British Geological Survey, Keyworth.

Davies, J. and Exley, C. (1992) 'Hydrochemical character of the main aquifer units of central and northeastern Bangladesh and possible toxicity of groundwater to fish and humans', *BGS Technical Report WD/92/43R* and *Supplement WD/92/44R*.

Guha Mazumder, D. N., Haque, R., Ghosh, N., De, B. K., Santra, A., Chakraborty, D. and Smith, A. H. (1998) Arsenic levels in drinking water and the prevalence of skin lesions in West Bengal, India, *International Journal of Epidemiology*, **27**, pp. 871–77.

Kinniburgh, D. G. and Smedley, P. L. (eds) (2001) *Arsenic Contamination of Groundwater in Bangladesh*, British Geological Survey Technical Report WC/00/19, British Geological Survey, Keyworth.

Islam, F. S., Gault, A. G., Boothman, C., Polya, D. A., Charnock, J. M., Chatterjee, D. and Lloyd, J. R. (2004) Role of metal-reducing bacteria in arsenic release from Bengal delta sediments, *Nature*, **430**, pp. 68–71.

Meharg, A. A. (2005) *Venomous Earth*, Macmillan, Basingstoke and New York.

Ravenscroft, P., McArthur, J. M. and Hoque, B. A. (2001) Geochemical and palaeohydrological controls on pollution of groundwater by arsenic, in Chappell, W. R., Abernathy, C. O. and Calderon, R. L. (eds) *Arsenic Exposure and Health Effects IV*, Elsevier, Oxford, pp. 53–77.

Smith, A. H., Hopenhayn-Rich, C., Bates, M. N., Goeden, H. M., Hertz-Picciotto, I., Duggan, H. M., *et al.* (1992) Cancer risks from arsenic in drinking water, *Environmental Health Perspectives*, **97**, pp. 259–67.

Websites

Arsenic Crisis Newsletter http://groups.yahoo.com/group/arsenic-crisis/ (accessed January 2006).

London Arsenic Group http://www.es.ucl.ac.uk/research/lag/as (accessed January 2006).

Acknowledgements

Several people helped significantly with the preparation of this topic. Margaret Andrews Deller encouraged the author to read early reports of the widespread nature of arsenic contamination and the need for comprehensive testing of well water in several low-income countries. *Water and well-being* stemmed from her suggestion. John Watson provided the newspaper report at the start of Chapter 1, which concerned the death by accidental arsenic poisoning of members of the Outhwaite family, from whom he is descended. Albert Ilges of the American Water Works Association provided comprehensive information about arsenic-remediation technology.

Grateful acknowledgement is made to the following sources for permission to reproduce material within this book.

Cover photo copyright © Dieter Telemans/Panos.

Figure 1.1 Copyright © David Kinniburgh/British Geological Survey; *Figure 1.2* Reproduced by permission of the British Geological Survey © NERC. All rights reserved, IPR/73-08C; *Figure 2.1(a)* Copyright © Wellcome Photo Library; *Figure 2.5* Copyright © Geoscience Features Picture Library; *Figure 2.7* By permission of Professor Richard Wilson, Harvard University, www.hsph.harvard.edu/arsenic/arsenic; *Figure 2.8* Guha Mazumder, D. N., Haque, R., Ghosh, N. et al. (1998) Arsenic levels in drinking water and the prevalence of skin lesions in West Bengal, India, **27**, *International Journal of Epidemiology*. Copyright © 1998 International Epidemiology Association; *Figure 2.9* Smith, A. H. et al. (1992) Cancer risks from arsenic in drinking water, *Environmental Health Perspectives*, **97**, US Department of Health & Human Services, National Institute of Environmental Health Services; *Figure 3.1* Copyright © US Geological Survey; *Figures 3.5(a), 3.6, 3.8, 3.9, 3.10, 3.11, 3.12, 3.14, 3.15 and 3.17(a)* Kinniburgh, D. G. and Smedley, P.L. (eds) (2001) *Arsenic contamination of groundwater in Bangladesh*, BGS and DPHE, British Geological Survey Technical Report WC/00/19, British Geological Survey, Keyworth; *Figure 3.5(b)* Reprinted from Umitsu, M. (1993) Late Quaternary sedimentary environments and landforms in the Ganges delta, *Sedimentary Geology*, **83**, Elsevier Science; *Figures 3.16 and 3.17(b)* Reprinted from Chappell, W. R., Abernathy, C. O. and Calderon, R. L. (2001) *Arsenic Exposure and Health Effects*, Vol 4, Health effects – non cancer, pp. 53–77. Copyright © with permission from Elsevier; *Figure 3.18* by permission of BDG Whymap; *Figure 3.19(a)*: Copyright © United Nations; *Figure 3.19(b)* Copyright © NASA; *Figure 4.1*: ICCDR,B, Health and Demographic Surveillance System-Matlab, Registration of health and demographic events (1983 to 2005) workbook. Dhaka: ICCDDR,B, 2007; *Figures 5.1 and 5.2* Copyright © John McArthur.

Every effort has been made to contact copyright holders. If any have been inadvertently overlooked, the publishers will be pleased to make the necessary arrangements at the first opportunity.

Index

Index entries and page numbers in **bold** are key terms defined, along with important terms, in the Glossary. Page numbers in *italics* refer to items mainly, or wholly, in a figure or table.